Writing in Hope

_Northampton Hope Centre
Creative Writing Group_

ii

Published in 2019 by Northampton Hope Centre
www.northamptonhopecentre.org.uk
office@northamptonhopecentre.org.uk
Registered Charity Number 1015743

Northampton Hope Centre Creative Writing Group
Writing in Hope
ISBN 978-1-5272-4182-4

Cover design and typesetting by Strelka   www.strelka.co.uk

Printed and bound by Belmont Press, Sheaf Close, Lodge Farm,
Harlestone Road, Northampton NN5 7UZ, England

Hope Centre

Robin Burgess, C.E.O., Northampton Hope Centre

———

Northampton Hope Centre has been helping people experiencing some of the worst forms of poverty, exclusion and homelessness for over 45 years. Over the years Hope has moved on from being a simple soup kitchen into being an organisation, based around a 6 day a week day centre drop-in, which enables people to move on in their lives, becoming less dependent on charity or welfare, and more able to stand on their own feet. We are an agency very much loved and valued by the people of Northampton, who are our main funders and ardent allies.

Being marginalised and excluded means that our service users often have no access to anything other than the simplest level of existence – eating, sleeping – and spending lots of time managing challenging issues in their lives like addictions and mental ill-health. We work to help people cope with and address all of these things through our caring, devoted staff and volunteers.

Hope continues to develop and add new services. Over the years social enterprises have been added, giving work opportunities; we also work to improve and promote healthy behaviours. We have become an agency actively training professionals in social work, social care and occupational therapy, and we have become involved in campaigning for justice and fairness in how people in poverty are treated by government and official agencies, and sometimes by the general public.

For several years Hope has also been providing a range of additional services that offer more. Art and creativity are a key part of this offer. Being able to paint, do some gardening, perhaps a fitness class or to express yourself through writing, gives people burdened with complex pressures and challenges that drag them down, an opportunity to step outside those issues, even for an hour. These services, usually volunteer led, provide a small breathing space for people with very limited alternative opportunities to do more than simply survive. Participating in creative activities helps free the mind, offers solace, and opens up talents that have often been hidden or simply impossible to realise with no money or time available to them through poverty. These opportunities help improve their confidence and self-worth, battered as these are by the pressures of living life with no money and problems like anxiety, depression and addiction that this brings.

The Hope Centre cherishes the work our volunteers do, in creating opportunities like the creative writing group, that offer so much to our service users. This book of writing from the creative writing group is expressive of the talents, emotions, experiences and qualities of our service users, people often ignored or stereotyped or otherwise dismissed by society. The writing they produce, and the voice it gives them, is invaluable in challenging these prejudices and assumptions about those forced to live on the margins.

Northampton Hope Centre
Creative Writing Group

Dave Blake, Volunteer, Northampton Hope Centre

———

The idea for a creative writing group came from Lorna Robjohns, a Hope Centre volunteer for many years, and she continues to support a former teaching colleague, Dave Blake, who has led the activity since June 2012. The group meets fortnightly through certain periods of the year and, at the time of writing, there have been 125 sessions. Generally, participant numbers are from four to eight, with some very regular attendees providing the cornerstone of the group.

Each self-contained session is based around a theme (e.g. a memory of place, a folk tale, truth) and the starting points vary. Examples are a list of words, idioms or quotations, a picture, a told story, a song lyric or an object. The concentration on one theme in each hour and a half session provides a focus for the writing, generates energy in the activities and also takes account of the fact that there is no guarantee of continuity in participants' attendance.

Within the timescale, there is usually opportunity for focused talk, some short burst writing and the writing of a longer piece, although this is often limited to about 30 minutes. Only very occasionally is any writing further developed and completed at home. The stimulus for the final task is quite an open one within the theme, with the aim being for each author to have choice in how they approach the subject.

A vital element of the group is the sharing aloud of the writing produced and the authors are very supportive of the output of each other. The atmosphere is such that new members feel sufficiently comfortable to read out their work and there is an appreciation that each individual has his or her own style and will often be drawing on very personal experiences.

The emphasis of the group is very much on encouraging people to express themselves in writing without them being too concerned about issues such as handwriting and spelling. What you will read in this book are the participants' first draft reactions to the tasks encountered. After each session, everyone's work is typed up so that authors can receive a copy of their own pieces and for display within the Hope Centre, which attracts interest and comment from visitors. At this stage, the writing will have been spell checked and sometimes have had punctuation strengthened. Except for these elements and the layout on the page, there is no attempt to redraft or further edit the work.

We are delighted that Northampton author Alan Moore has provided the foreword for *Writing in Hope*. He is a great supporter of Hope Centre and visited the Creative Writing Group to speak about growing up in the town, his writing career and his views on a broad range of issues.

He is the author of a number of internationally renowned graphic novels, including *Watchmen*, *V for Vendetta* and *The League of Extraordinary Gentlemen*. He has written short story collections, such as *Voice of the Fire*, and novels including the three part *Jerusalem*, set in and around Northampton. His screenplay for *The Show* has been produced as a feature film, one in which he also acts, and once again the town is the backdrop to the action.

During the morning at Hope Centre, he read and discussed the work of the group members, writing inspired by the local area and personal experiences. He was full of encouragement when speaking to his fellow authors and the visit was both a memorable experience and a great boost for the writers.

This book provides an opportunity to reach a wide readership and it is hoped those who read the work of the group's members will catch a glimpse of the talents and lives of others.

Foreword
No Such Thing As Bad Language
Alan Moore

———

Trainer, in the words of Tom Waits, was a raindog: moon-faced with heartbroken eyes like bruises, straggly moustache and pencil outline of a beard, providing *The Big Issue* from his doorway pitch just down from Marks & Spencer's, back when both he and the retail outlet were alive. He wore a permanent expression of incredulous dismay at the world's unexpected weight; at the impossibility of happiness, of love, of a warm bed, of everything. He was a likeable and decent man who'd been an unsuspecting baby once and hadn't known that all of this was going to happen.

There was an occasion when the trouble that was Trainer's weather-system seemed to have become torrential and had soaked him to the bone, crouched in his recess, staring fixedly at Tesco's or the abyss. What had happened was the commonplace, routine, and always unbelievable event that will occur during the lifetime of most mammals. Trainer's mum was dead. One might think that would be enough, but simple destitution is a thing of mounting complications. Trying to do anything, even an ordinary human job like mourning a lost parent, is a prospect of increasing difficulty that can easily make an already dreadful situation much, much worse.

The thing was, while his mother's death was devastating, it brought with it the far more upsetting notion of her funeral. His family had no idea that he was living on the streets. How could he turn up for the service in his ratty fleece and his *Big Issue* lanyard, without trading all the shame that he felt sure would be in their eyes for the crushed humiliation in his own? He couldn't just not go, this was his mother's funeral, but he couldn't go like this. He'd have to get a suit. But there was no way that he could afford a suit, so it was better that he didn't go. But then, he couldn't just not go, this was his mother's funeral. You may already have an inkling where all this is heading.

Trainer tried to nick a suit. Of course he did. And Trainer was a raindog, so of course it didn't work. It turns out that to mooch around the racks of a gents' outfitters while dressed like he was doesn't tend to put the average store-detective at their ease. It turns out that to nick a suit successfully, it's best that you're already wearing one.

It doesn't seem that there were any charges pressed – how could you hear a mitigating circumstance like that and think that further punishment was warranted, unless you were perhaps a Dalek? – but the crumpled map of Trainer's face suggested that this was no consolation. He was still glued to his Abington Street doorway, suitless, bootless, and his mum was still dead. Hence the concussed gaze, glistening cheeks and unstrung puppet posture on that cloudy afternoon. Yeah, that's the look. That's the heartless austerity street-furniture that we're expected to get used to; that the council notices invite us, cordially, to ignore.

Faced with a hurt like that, with the hit-by-a-bus disaster of it all, our standard Kleenex-box of reassurances is obviously less than useless. No one much likes being told to "cheer up, it might never happen" when it's patently already effing happened. No one wants to hear about the worse things going on at sea, and the "one day" when we'll look back on this and laugh is never going to arrive, except for, possibly, hyenas who can't help it. Simply put, what can you say?

The best that I could do was talk about how it had been when my own mum had died, up at a not-yet-nightmarish St. Edmund's Hospital where I'd been born some forty-something years before – and, yes, a blue plaque would be nice. I told him that when Sylvia Doreen had gone, I'd been left with enormous, painful, pointless and banal emotions tumbling around inside me and had absolutely nothing I could put them to or do with them. They were no use to me, to anyone around me, and especially were no use to my mum. If I was going to restore her with some hopelessly unlikely magic wand, if I was going to somehow bring her back and mend this loss, then I was going to need materials that were a lot more versatile and powerful than ordinary anguish, which builds nothing but depressed mud pies. I would need words, but, luckily, I was some sort of writer.

Writing, in the real world, is the chocolate teapot of professions in that it's no good for anything remotely practical. It won't rewire your house. It won't arrange a mortgage, get you drunk, or do a bloody thing about your diabetes. If you should get set upon by ruffians, writing looks the other way and doesn't lift a finger. As a lifestyle choice, it still remains the quickest, surest way to starve, particularly poetry. If there's enough of it you might kill the odd fly, but other than that writing seems to have no valuable application anywhere in the material universe. But for the universe that's inside each of us, the universe of 'I' that's arguably bigger and of more immediate importance to us, writing is gigantic and unbeatable, omnipotent. It can do anything.

What I did was take all the thoughts and memories and feelings that were going through a rinse-cycle inside my well-proportioned skull, and turned them into a long piece of writing, arguably a poem, that was called 'The Birth Caul'. I thought it was quite good, but whether it was good or not was not the point: the point was that I'd written it. The point was that I'd taken something miserable inside me and unloaded it into a form that was no longer hurtful to me. I'd changed it to something that might possibly be useful to somebody going through a similar ordeal, and in the process I'd carved a memorial to my mum which, with a bit of luck, might last as long as marble.

I suggested Trainer might try the same strategy, and he said the same things that nearly everybody says when faced with that suggestion. He said that he couldn't write, had never written anything more complicated than a shopping list, because his writing wasn't good enough. Which raised the question, "Good enough for who?" For some literary critic in the Sunday papers? For an inexplicably unhappy English teacher who has very probably been dead for years? Writing – and I think I say this with authority – can ultimately only be judged "good enough" by she or he that wrote it, the one person who can say if their big pile of words did what they wanted it to do. It also has the benefit of not requiring much equipment or technology more costly than a pencil and a piece of paper. Writing doesn't exclude anybody, even Trainer. I told him that he should have a go, just write down everything he felt about his mum. What had he got to lose? What had he ever had to lose? He said perhaps he would, delivered in a tone of voice implying that he definitely wouldn't.

The next time that I saw him, then, was a surprise. He was still there in the same clothes, same doorway and same life, but otherwise he was completely different. He looked stunned and wonderstruck, like somebody abducted by a gang of mermaids. He'd done what I said, he told me. Not expecting anything but disappointment, he'd sat down to write whatever scarce words he could summon on the subject of his mum, perhaps a clumsy line or two if he was lucky, and had found himself possessed. Uncorked, the verbal wine had all come pouring out of him, page after page. "I couldn't stop." As for his literary style, he understood now that it didn't matter. He'd spoken the truth of him, and what is true is never clumsy. He'd discovered something that the homeless are denied, something they lack as much as they lack shelter, dignity or a hot dinner, this being a voice.

x

I don't know if he ever showed his words to anybody. I don't know what happened to them; don't know if they even still exist. I hope so, but that isn't the important issue. The important thing is that once in a life where he could not express the million things inside him, Trainer got to sing the ballad of himself. He found a voice, one that had been his all along and that no store security or magistrate could take away from him. And when he got his chance to speak, he didn't talk about his problems or his grievances. He said how much he loved his mum.

It was a year or three thereafter that I went down to the Hope Centre to meet with the creative writing group. The place is wonderful and necessary, filled with wonderful and necessary people that have offered refuge to good mates of mine when they were stuck in one of the bad patches that there seem to be so many more of these days. I was talking to the group about one of the only things I know for sure, which is that writing is your medicine, your telescope, your shield, your weapon. Writing is a supernatural power. Properly honed and polished, it potentially can take you anywhere and almost heal your broken heart. Having the writer's habit of recycling a useful anecdote, I told them about Trainer and his testament. That's when Caroline Atterwill gently informed me he was gone; had given up his mortal pitch; been moved on by an ultimate policeman. That's a lot more than a rotten shame, but at least Trainer got to try life without the mute-button on. At very least, he got to speak his piece.

And now we've the first published fruits of that creative writing group for our consideration, work by people who've picked up the ball that Trainer was so flabbergasted by and run with it, or at least punted it a good sight further down the field. Here in Northampton, whereat W.H. Davies scribbled down his *Autobiography of a Super-tramp* as another vagrant in the reading room of the town library, with this marvellous collection we have once more managed to transform the everyday manure of life to gold. You'll find writings in here that are indignant, melancholy, luminous and very, very funny, but you will not find a solitary word that doesn't represent a massive leap of optimism, faith and self-belief before pen first kissed paper. You'll find nothing that somebody didn't care enough about to write it down. These are all individuals who have found their voices, and this is the first performance of their choir. I hope that you enjoy the music half as much as I did.

The Authors

———

Thank you to the following authors, who have given their permission for their writing to be included in this book. In addition, we have included pieces from four people we have been unable to locate, assuming that, as their work had previously been displayed publicly, they too would have agreed to its publication in this form.

Ambrose Doherty	Michael Derrig
Caroline Atterwill	Peta Trigger
Richard Jones	Dee Linaken
Richard Baker	Mark Trenbeth
Kelvin Thompson	Adam Bowles
Richard Cotton	Carl Williams
Sean Nelson	Gordon
Emma Page	Claire
Emma Dawson	Matthew
Robert Billingham	Liam

Thank you to the members of the Hope Centre Art Group who contributed illustrations: Richard Baker (A View From Eden and Station Vending Machine) and Mitchell Watson (Meeting At The Bus Stop).

Contents

———

And To Close...

Reflections of Self

Mentor

Caroline Atterwill

———

After I left school without exams to fall back on, I just sort of drifted through life, walking down all the wrong paths, drink, drugs, violence and the streets, and basically pure disrespect. Well, I never really had any reason to show respect to anyone. It was a case of "if I don't look after myself then who will?" and I did a lot of wrong 'uns without caring about the repercussions. But that all changed one day when I was down the old soup kitchen, in my usual messed up state, my head in a bowl of soup, when a woman noticed me. After a while we struck up a friendship and as I became more lucid I started to realise and appreciate this lady more and more, and all the time and effort she had put into me, time and effort that I hadn't afforded myself. And this lady is my Lorna.

As the years followed, through my ups and downs (which there have been many), she has always been there, either for advice or to lend a hand or just for the telling off I have needed. I am very glad to say that I am not the only down and out she has helped through the years and I am privileged to know her. To this day I will never quite understand why a lady like this would fish me out of a bowl of soup, but one thing is sure, if she hadn't then I might still be there now.

Friendship

Ambrose Doherty

———

At a moment in time, when all seems so difficult,
And darkness becomes colour
And it's all that you see,
Can you call on a friend?
If yes be the answer, then you're lucky indeed.
In joy and in sadness,
In strife and success,
A friend will be with you to share all that goes on.
To lift you if needed, with supports all in place,
To catch you from falling with a comforting embrace,
To celebrate achievement and victories that arrive,
To remind you when needed,
It's good being alive!!

4

An Island
Richard Baker

———

Do we all see life through the same set of eyes?
Can we hear the same music in one set of ears?
We all see suffering, but are the levels of pain the same
in all the viewing pairs of eyes?
Empathy can only detach itself from its sister, Sympathy,
when Being can be as true as Seeing.
If we all truly felt and saw what pain others suffer,
we could not tolerate the discordant notes
and painful scars the world and life subject us to.
Nature therefore sedates us with light for our own eyes,
and music for our own ears, so that we can survive troubles all around.
Maybe John Donne was correct in saying no man is an island.
Sometimes we need to be isolated,
to escape the tormented lives of others.
Book me a one-way ticket to my own deserted island.

Church Pew

Emma Page

———

Can you see that lonely girl sat at the back of the church?
I can!

And as I look closer I can see her tears, then I realise it's me. What are the tears for? I ask myself. Pain and anger, loss and sadness. Why all the emotions?

Well, I'll tell you now, my life has hit an all time low. I'm always at the bottom of the bottle of cider, feeling lost and alone as my house is gone, my children too, through no fault of my own, for the sake of another.

All of a sudden I wake with a jump and realise that today I see my children as I do every week and remember that all this pain is actually reality but now in the past, as slowly but surely I'm climbing back up the ladder and into the light.

Thank you God for your strength to help overcome this bad past. I now go to church and I sit not at the back but now at the front as I can see a positive future.

Alter Ego

Caroline Atterwill

———

Caroline is funny, articulate, generous, trustworthy and an all-round good egg. Caroline is devious, sly, always looking for earners, acid tongued, and always looking out for herself.

Reading this, you could think that I was talking about two people but both are me. It could be a good day or a bad day, pay day or pay out day, sunshine or rain, cold or warm. All are a part of me, depending on these variables.

Alter ego?

The Mistress Of Disguise
Claire

———

Many a time I have kept my feelings under disguise,
in many different ways, shapes and forms.
In an attempt to hide the way I may feel,
my true emotions I will try to conceal.
It may sometimes be in the way I dress,
the way I act and talk,
my feelings I suppress.

A Brief Trawl

Ambrose Doherty

———

A brief trawl through the conflagration that disguises itself, quite convincingly at times, as a sane mind. I find myself unable to form any semblance of cognitive thought. So much for sanity.

My handwriting is almost illegible and as a consequence the only analogy that appeals is - having spent most of my adult life doing so to the obvious multitude, I may as well continue.

Just keep up the act, my son. If they ain't sussed it yet, they never will.

Window

Richard Baker

———

A person looks at life from many perspectives and sees nothing of meaningful connections to events, people and places. View events, people and places from one window and over time a pattern emerges and a clear picture appears. The world from the same window stays the same, yet changes beyond recognition.

We all remember the view from a childhood window when we were not allowed out. The world seemed so small and contained. Nothing existed beyond that view, yet we were impatient to see further, to grow and explore.

As we get older and see more, we sometimes long for that small cosy world of long lost childhood, when everything was contained and content and when we knew every face that passed by. We long for change and excitement but not so close that the past disappears from memory. A life without memory is a life not lived. But a life with no progress is not a life worth living.

The past, present and future must all remain relevant to us to make us a whole person, and we must try to leave the contented world we joined. Then, our children may experience the same progression.

What Is Truth?

Ambrose Doherty

———

The eternal question, or perhaps not.
It is a most unfortunately unfathomable concept
subject to mind-boggling extremes of ultimately false perception.
Why?
What is truth?
Indeterminate, open to scrutiny beyond reasonable doubt.
But whose doubt?
What's feasible in its interpretation to one
may often not be to another.
What is truth not?
The answer to everything,
and that's its great shame, because it wishes it so.
In the end of all examination
Truth is a personal search to discover oneself
and prove we are worthy to embrace,
To embrace all that truth is. Can we withstand its many facets
and collisions with those who would have dominion over its power?
There lies its purpose for those that believe.
It is truly eternal,
but have confidence in it,
for the alternative is chaos and a feeling of fear.
Embrace its confusion but do stray from its value.

When Eve

Robert Billingham

———

When Eve had led her lord away
  And Cain k.o.'d his brother,
The stars and flowers, the poets say,
Smiled at one another.

Individuality

Emma Dawson

———

I like being independent. I enjoy feeling better about myself. I like listening, I like talking, I like most things. Individuality is very personal. Listen, I'm going to tell you something. My favourite person is not me. It's the person I would like to be.

As personal and as individual as it is, I would like my freedom. I would like the idea of doing things for myself. Guess what? I'm going to tell you that when I get there, I will feel more able, much better and stronger. Why? Because I need a better piece of time that will enable me to progress, so I can get better in my abilities. I'm not only a talented ice skater, I like drawing – I'm an artist and my favourite day of the week is Wednesday when I do art.

What I want to say to you is that I'm a good person. My individuality is me and my independence starts right here! Hip, hip, hooray.

Technology

Sean Nelson

I find the thought of staring at a screen and relaying my thoughts (especially personal ones) very disconcerting.

There is something very clinical and soulless about this exercise, as I like to look people dead straight in the eyes when communicating. Of course, that is not always possible, hence the telephone.

Whatever happened to good old handwritten letters?

A person's true expression,

the essence of the person laid bare

in their own unique handwritten way.

Karma

Caroline Atterwill

———

I'm not a religious person and I haven't been christened. I did ask what was the reason for this and I was told rather than having religion thrust upon me, I had the choice to decide for myself when I got older. But the whole church thing never appealed to me so for the last few years I've been trying to live the karma lifestyle. What goes around, comes around, whether it be good or bad because it works both ways.

It's taken me a few years to figure this out though but now, when possible, I try to do positive things, either in my behaviour or lending a helping hand. And so far it has been a success but on rare occasions karma goes out the window, and so nearly have I.

Other People

———

Everything Is Funny As Long As It Happens To Someone Else

Caroline Atterwill

————

An old person falls over - funny.
A dog slipping on ice - funny.
Watching a drunken man unsteady on his legs - funny.
A baby eating something sour for the first time – funny.
Kids throwing snowballs at each other – funny.
Teachers telling off a classmate – funny.
A fat man running for a bus – funny.
A dog pulling its master over – funny.
Someone doing a skateboard trick and falling off – funny.

I have laughed at all these things in my life and my instinct
has always been the same – funny.
But would I feel the same if it happened to me?

Laughter
Ambrose Doherty

———

Searching into the depths of a memory in childhood, as I recall, there wasn't much to laugh about then. The three day week, gas rationing, the miners on strike again. Yet somehow all those around me, mostly friends and family, were all in it together and made the best of the prevailing circumstances.

Darkness never prevailed as we all shared the good and the not so, as we were all in the same boat and what's more, most of us were rowing in the same direction, and when we weren't, someone would make us laugh just to maintain morale and a sense of togetherness. That was mostly my Uncle Martin, as when he laughed it was so infectious we all couldn't help but join in the fun. Happy days!

Title

Caroline Atterwill

———

I've got a title, the best in the world,
Not king, not queen, not duke nor earl.
I am Auntie, "The Auntie", in fact, "Caroline"
With a niece and a nephew
Whose bloodline is mine.
The cute and the cocky, together they grow,
Their adventure beginning
And nobody knows
What life they'll be handed or worked, sweat and tears.
Their progress and promise I see through the years.
Their amazing achievements.
Mistakes will be made,
But learning through life,
That's the past, that will fade.
I love these two aliens that became to exist.
Thank you my family, my Sally, my sis.

Summer Babysitting

Caroline Atterwill

———

I was babysitting later that day and I couldn't wait. And because it was summer, the weather was beautiful and there was nothing I would rather do than see my niece, who's 5, and nephew, 9, because I only usually get to see them when it's a special occasion such as birthdays and Christmas.

When I got to my sister's house and the others left, we all pondered what to do. Well, the sun was scorching and in the shed were two water pistols so it didn't take long to figure out what we were going to do. And so we began chasing each other around the garden, taking it in turns with the water pistols, squirting one another with such motivation and, unluckily for me, accuracy.

After a lot of squealing, laughing and general messing around, we were all soaked through. So we all had to rush upstairs and get changed into dry clothes as quickly as possible before my sister returned. But as I was rushing around trying to find Jess's t-shirt, I heard the door opening downstairs and for some reason, I didn't know why, I felt like a naughty child just caught doing something wrong.

They came up the stairs. Wet clothes scattered on the floor, drawers open and the dry clothes flung. At this point my sister took over and within minutes everyone was dry and the mess cleared up. I don't know how she did it. That day was a wonderful day.

My Hero

Ambrose Doherty

———

There he lay all shiny with light,
    dressed to the nines in his Sunday best,
looking serene at the gathering's behest.
All was as ordered and nought out of place
for this was the time above all the rest.
Flashes of light, yet no light at all,
echoes of sound that bounced through us all.
A glistening appears in all there that day,
of teardrops and sorrow to their own dismay.
For me, no such nonsense showed its shadow upon me,
as having judged to unawareness through youth,
only I there present was truly aware of the truth.
One more look before darkness and the last pledge of love
for the passing of Daddy into the abyss above.
Into safeness we pledge and you deserve it, I'm sure,
For the heart that has left us I know to be pure.

Goodbye Grandad
Emma Page

———

There was a little girl called Emma who suffered a terrible loss. She was four years old, soon to be five in a few weeks, on March 4th. She was hit hard by this as her granddad Ivan Maholoninski had virtually brought her up. Her mum worked days and at night she would go out, sometimes with friends.

Ivan had died in hospital. He had gangrene from an old gunshot wound he got back in World War 2, back in his homeland Ukraine. The last time she saw him (or so she thought) was when she went to say her goodbyes, as he was very sick and tired, losing his fight. He kissed her on the head and said a few words. Then, when she had gone, he fell peacefully to sleep, this time forever.

Some weeks after this, Emma woke up every night screaming and crying. This went on for a few weeks. When her mum went to her, all she would do was point to the end of the bed and say, "Grandad." Then one night she woke screaming so loud that she woke her mum with a startling fright. As her mum ran into the bedroom, a very cold breeze whooshed through the room. Emma was sat bolt upright and was very distressed and frightened when she told her mum that Grandad had put his hands over her mouth. At this point, her mother called out, "Dad, Emma is safe and so are we," (meaning herself and her husband). "Please leave us alone as you are frightening her. We will be fine, Dad. Go and rest." With that, the cold air became warm and Emma was calm. Both her and her mum then spotted two balls of light in the corner of the room and they just disappeared.

From that night on, Emma never woke again. Her mum believes that after her dad had died he would try and say "Shh" and comfort her as he once had when he was in the land of the living. That is the close bond they once had and always will till the day they will once again be together.

Bus Driver

Caroline Atterwill

———

The early morning starts too early.
The same routes over and over and over.
Soggy cheese sandwiches with a quick ciggy break
then back on the humid, stifling bus.
My belly's getting bigger and my seat smaller.
My sagging breasts are virtually steering the wheel.
Only the odd sight, the dog squatting, the cyclist whizzing past.
And at the end of it all,
a bus ride home.

Bus Driver

Ambrose Doherty

———

My God, is that the time already? Sleep has flown again. I hate this awakening, so loud and so now! Really, is it time, again?

Well the ritual begins , the wash and all that. Shit, no toothpaste again. I'll kill that lad. Most kids have a sweet tooth, his is a toothpaste tooth. I need to have a word with him, but no time.

Uniform on, shoes shining, head for the shift, time moving on.

Eight hours of this. Can I endure, with all it entails, footfalls and all? Think about parking at the end of the day, and the walk home so you can say another one done and more to endure, but look at your family and know that it's worth it. To be sure.

Mr Right

Caroline Atterwill

———

When watching the weather forecast, if they said it would be sunny, he would wear a rain mac and carry an umbrella because he knew that it would rain, and he was right.

When he went shopping with his list in his hand and the correct money in his pocket, the cashier accidentally overcharged him and, with an air of arrogance about him, Mr Right went through the receipt with the cashier and, of course, he was right.

Whilst walking back from the shop, a young boy bumped into him and Mr Right looked down and in a deep voice said, "Is there anything you would like to say?" to which the young boy answered, "I ain't done nothing wrong."

With a disappointed look, Mr Right responded, "I haven't done anything wrong," to which the boy replied, "Nor have I" and off he went.

A Knight Of Disaster

Richard Jones

———

Sir Guy the Gangly, ancestor of Sir Gullible of the Flat Tower, was in fact the Unknown Knight of the Round Table. Largely forgotten due to his blunders, he had an infamously bad sense of direction. When King Arthur sent out his knights to seek the Holy Grail, Sir Guy bought a cheap, fake map of the known world and headed south instead of east. He believed he had found the grail's resting place when he discovered a mountain that looked like a table, for where else could the Cup of God be found.

Upon returning from his fruitless adventures, Sir Guy made many efforts to retrieve "fallen cutlery" at the banquet held in his honour, just so he could hide under the table.

Other blunders included:

He returned with an axe when Arthur sent him to the blacksmith's to get Excalibur sharpened.

His efforts at getting the Round Table varnished ended up with it getting re-carved into a square.

And, when the Saxons launched their last attack, he accidentally left Camelot's gates open.

The Specialist

Richard Jones

———

In the kingdom of Gelderland, Old King Cole, who was beloved by his people and loved back, used to enjoy going out and meeting his loyal subjects. But eventually he became too old and frail for his frequent walks. Luckily, however, a new technology had recently arrived in the kingdom, a machine people called an engine, that could turn wheels, and some people had even started riding these machines.

Upon hearing this, Old King Cole summoned his best engineers and asked them to see if this new machine could be used to help him. Unfamiliar with the new technology, the engineers called upon a specialist who knew about it.

Surprised and overjoyed at the royal request, the specialist designed a huge throne with one of these engines hidden inside it. So pleased with his machine was he, King Cole gave the specialist the honour of being the sole operator of the new vehicle.

From that day on, the specialist would tell his friends that he was the power behind the throne.

Pitch

Ambrose Doherty

———

There is always one that creates a memory, usually in company that share in the memory, which, as I usually find, is dependent on a simple keyword from out of left field, and the floodgates open. Not always welcome as readiness or anticipation, awareness or preparedness, were pitched without intention to do so.

One of many such occasions happened recently and fortunately sufficient time has passed so as to ensure happiness and fond remembrance. A friend lost before his time and of a significance in my life that few others could hold a candle to. A sage, for sure, kind and gentle of soul, yet, as we all can be, contrary, stubborn and outright annoying from time to time. He had a pitch, one that led to the most memorable day of my recent life.

It happened one simple Wednesday when on his pitch, my friend was approached for a Big Issue. No money changed hands, a payment was made with something beyond fiscal value.

Two tickets to the Silverstone Classic, 2011.

The best day of our shared lives and cherished to this day.

Pitched on his pitch by my dear friend Simon.

Thanks, Man.

A Pat On The Back

Kelvin Thompson

———

A pat on the back is a nice thing to get
It's like winning some money after a bet.
It's nice to know someone likes your worth.
When no-one says thanks, it sometimes hurts.

A pat on the back makes you work very hard
If no-one says thanks, it makes you mad.
It's like saying well done when the job is done
A pat on the back when the battle is won.

This poem deserves a pat on the back
I wrote it in just ten minutes flat.
It's not too short and not too long
Give me a pat as I end this song.

Enemies
Michael Derrig

———

The Oscar Wilde quote I really like is-
"Always forgive your enemies; nothing annoys them so much."

As well as being funny, it is also true. The more you forgive them and ignore their behaviour, the more frustrated they become. They have nowhere to go with their bile and vitriol if you are pleasant and forgiving, or give the appearance of being forgiving.

Wallpaper Of Life

Michael Derrig

———

When he looked back at his life, the disappointments and triumphs, he had the thought that his life, and everyone's life, consisted of many different layers and textures. Rather like layers of different kinds of wallpaper on a wall. Just like wallpaper, with each individual history and place in time, that could be a symbol of a person's life and experience – good or bad.

He thought that what he was doing was like revisiting the past, and stripping back his history, like stripping back the wallpaper to see where he came from.

Aliens

Caroline Atterwill

———

How ironic that over the last few years or so people have been obsessed with alien landings and alien beings and basically everything alien.

There's been technology made especially for the purpose of searching for and finding aliens. And always wanting more thrown at the discovery of such creatures than I could ever imagine, I dread to think how much time, effort and money went into these findings. Billions of pounds and expertise when later in 2018 over 600 were left out at sea, drifting for over a week, facing an unknown future. For the sake of just a few more thousand light years and a couple of "bidilly bobs" and "dobedoos", they would have been treated like royalty.

Tell Me Teacher

Robert Billingham

————

Tell me teacher
with what to compete
when homo sapien
is obsolete.
When wars are fought
with Satan's fork
produced from a machine
that is just a trick.
When satellites guide us
through our time
with sardonic eyes
better than mine.
Tell me teacher
with what to fight
when a new night
overshadows the light.

The Comprehension And Preservation of Peace
(based on a mural by Banksy)

Richard Jones

———

An old town…a pained town. Hatred and division marred its long history but peace had eventually come. Its people, who were not always the cause of its hardships through history, were all too aware of how precious and fragile peace is.

In order to never forget, a series of murals were painted to symbolise this, with new ones painted as time changed.

It was because of this that, on a street corner, a new painting of the Dove of Peace with his olive branch was shown wearing body armour whilst in the sights of a gunman. For even peace has enemies.

Between Hope And Reality

Caroline Atterwill

―――――

This Banksy mural expresses both hope and reality with the white dove, an olive branch in its mouth, symbolising peace and this is where I wish the mural had finished.

But sometimes visions of peace have to be flipped to show more of the reality of life and, unfortunately, this is life because as he flies through the sky, there will always be a danger around every corner.

So always be prepared, for one day you may have the target on your chest and this will be the day you forgot your bullet proof vest.

Memories of Place

My Favourite Place In Northampton
Richard Jones

———

Being born in and growing up in Northampton means I know the place too well, but, ironically, there are also places that seem almost alien to me, which I guess is just the surprise of finding something new when you didn't think you either would or could.

I remember as a small child going with my mum to Weston Favell Centre and being dragged around Tesco's, and then hanging around waiting for the bus back, which was old fashioned and painted green (the old United Counties colour). That was a bit of an event – and a kind of a treat, as I'd usually get a new Lego toy if I was good – as dad usually did a big shop at the weekend while mum did the housework and cooked the Sunday dinner. The rest of the week, me and mum would use the local corner shop, normally on the way home from school.

Sometimes on a Sunday after dinner, we'd go down to Abington Park where I loved going on the old roundabout, even if it was a little dangerous (which is probably why it was removed). I remember one winter when it had snowed particularly heavily – back when it was almost guaranteed to snow at some point around the turn of the year, as opposed to being just cold and wet, and then getting surprised by snow in the middle of spring – we'd gone down to the park with our fairly large sledge, which was quite hard to miss, it being bright orange, and I had a bit of a scare when on one go I really thought I was going to end up in the frozen lake at the bottom.

One other thing I remember that I liked about the park was when they used to have a boating area near the old tower, which I also like as, while it at least looks like a medieval tower, its presence hints at the town's history.

The town I call home.

In Northampton
Ambrose Doherty

———

The day began as many others previously, and without doubt yet to come, had and will. The springtime rising of the sun was as always resplendent in its subtle ferocity. The daily grind, that he had come to call it, was somewhat lifted by the initial splendour.

Great, he assumed almost subconsciously, what will this appearingly positive day bring forth? He went to his beloved bay window and drew the curtains fully to expose the view of his undying passion – Northamptonshire County Cricket Club. He paused in an instant of recollection to try to fathom why this love had come about and sorrow dimmed his enthusiasm.

Was it really that long past? It was She. The passion was her fault entirely. It was her never-ending conviction and equally unending enthusiasm. Yes, indeed.

As he felt the bolt of memories oft times subdued, a chill rose from within, from the tip of his toes to the eventual rising of the hair on the back of his neck. It had all began with such innocence and anticipation, the turning of a page, a new beginning, a step in the right direction, etc, etc, etc.

Desperately, with all the energy he could muster, he tried to block out the images coursing through the echoing emptiness that was now awaiting him. Would it ever end? All his confidence and enthusiasm of moments ago dissolved into confusion. For She was no longer here to share it. She would never be again. He had to tell them, tell them all. Perhaps tomorrow.

Fire Eater

Dee Linaken

———

The circus entertainment was wonderful. I loved the drums, the costumes, the excitement of the acrobats but the best bit was the fire eaters. The way they stroked the flames across their limbs while contorting their bodies was heart stopping stuff, but they then starting eating it, spewing huge flames into the air while one encouraged a punter to light his cigarette from their mouth!

Our hands were sore from clapping, eyes shining with admiration and excitement. With their finale, they flicked their bodies through the air ending in an awkward looking pile of bodies, all extinguishing their fresh sticks at the same time.

Happy Memories Of A Place

Caroline Atterwill

———

My gran was a wonderful woman and visits with her were amazing. Every holiday, be it half term or summer holiday, we went down to Margate. Well, I say Margate but it was more Cliftonville, which was next door.

My heart jumped for joy every time I visited but this wasn't caused by the bright lights and loud noises of the machines or even the lido or Bembon Brothers. My heart leapt with the taste of boiled eggs and soldiers for breakfast, the whiff of the sea, and with the early morn the seagulls woke us. And, with the sand underfoot squidging through our toes and goosebumps from the freezing sea, these were the best days of my life.

The Most Interesting Journey Ever
Ambrose Doherty

———

The beauty of what's to come is laced with lyrical waxing. I plead latitude from all whom risk continuing. Here endeth the warning.

It all began long ago, however the memory, unlike others, has not mellowed. It's as fresh and vibrant as if it was yesterday. Four a.m. on a glorious Greek island, wide awake, my woman at my side, watching the glory that is the rising sun appear over a tranquil, thought provoking Mediterranean shore, gently lapping. Bedazzling to say the least.

Then realisation hit. No sleep from the night before, remnant of the consumption of a number of mind altering concoctions. Fifteen kilometres from our hotel with only a 90cc squeeze-and-go as transport. The nearest town 4ks away and no chance with the moped. Two stranded revellers. Decisions to be made. The residuals of the night before, if you see our dilemmas.

Let's walk it, it's already a wondrous morning. Away we trudged. After about three quarters of a kilometre a pick-up truck, already overloaded, stopped and an ancient Greek with a single-toothed smile picked us up. After tourist Greek and after a multitude of hand gestures, he agreed a lift to the nearest taxi rank.

Up one side of the mountain, no problems occurring. Over the crest, my heart rate and nerve whirring, to say the least. He was pumping the non-existent brakes for all he was worth, stopping us at last to ensure our remaining on Earth.

A Day In July At Billing

Kelvin Thompson

———

On a day in July a few weeks ago
the poetry group went to the pub,
Not only to talk about all that we know
but also to have some grub.
It was a nice day, the weather was kind
as we sat in the summer sun.
The swans swam around saying, "We don't mind
as long as you leave when you're done."
A coffee or tea was a welcome start
as we sat taking in the sights.
The lake, the birds just warmed my heart,
somehow it felt just right.
We talked and we laughed and had a good time.
"It's now time to eat," David said.
Some had fish or steak, with no wine,
or the all-day breakfast instead.
It was nice to see Les, he got some applause
for being about to make it.
Lorna, his wife, said after a pause,
he wasn't well but had to shake it.
The day was good, it didn't rain, and after a drink or two
We all said goodbye,
saying we'll come again,
God bless and good luck to you.

Yellowstone

Caroline Atterwill

———

My whole life has been growing up in Yellowstone in one of the remotest parts of the forest, so naturally me, Ma and Pa lived purely from nature. If we were hungry, Pa went out a-shooting deer, hare or pheasant. We always ate good after Ma had gutted, stripped and cooked the beast in the stewing pot. And like for many other people who live in the forest, it was a simple life. The men did the hunting and protecting, the women looked after the house.

But for me, the best time of the day is at night time when everything for the day is done and I sit on the stoop out back, winding down whilst watching the fireflies light up the whole of the skies. Beautiful.

Words, Idioms and Proverbs

Sticks And Stones

Mark Trenbeth

———

Sticks and stones
may break my bones
but words can never hurt me.

This is a saying that a lot of people use.
But I think it doesn't mean anything.
People say it but nobody likes to be talked about
Either behind their back or in front of them.

Most people like to be liked.

Words

Kelvin Thompson

———

Sticks and stones may break my bones
but words may never hurt me,
except when using mobile phones
and speaking to someone I can't see.
Nice words can make you feel good,
can give you quite a lift.
Some words make you touch some wood.
Some words are quite a gift.
Some words mean nothing when they're said.
It passes like the breeze.
Some words mean more when they are dead.
Some stay in time and freeze.
But keep talking, my good friend
and keep on writing too.
If you start one day, it will end.
Good luck in what you do.

There Is Nothing In A Caterpillar That Tells You It's Going To Be A Butterfly

Michael Derrig

———

There is nothing in a caterpillar that tells you it's going to be a butterfly.

This quotation by Buckminster Fuller is very clever and thought- provoking. What I take from it is that you never know what something may turn into just by looking at the tried and tested, as opposed to the novel and unsuspected.

Rather than relying on the logical approach, why not try the lateral and innovative approach?

Write Injuries In Sand, Kindnesses In Marble
(French proverb)
Sean Nelson

———

Injuries, hopefully, in time, will be erased, therefore to make them more vulnerable to the elements is self-healing and progressive.

To dwell on the positivity of "good" and kindness is a self medication for the soul, hence to be etched in marble, a far greater endurer of time, a constant to be used to draw strength from.

Good luck in what you do.

A Bad Air Day

Richard Jones

———

Tom didn't know what hit him.

As it happened, it was a first aid kit from a passing air sea rescue helicopter. Having tuned into the radio earlier, Tom had heard over the airwaves of an old airliner that was having to make an emergency landing at the nearest airport and a local RAF airfield had dispatched the air force to escort the stricken plane to safety.

The first aid kit did nothing but put a dent into the boot of Tom's car but the sudden stop caused an air pocket of compressed air in Tom's modified air gun to go off, setting off the air bags, putting a hole in the air conditioning, snapping off the aerial, and ruining the once airtight air bed he had kept in the boot.

Gathering his wits, and regretting the airy fairy modification on his air gun, Tom noticed a military aircraft approaching with airborne troops pouring out of it. Having landed, a couple of them came over to see what had happened. Tom told them of the accident and found out that the soldiers were on manoeuvres, practising an airlift, but the airhead pilot had flown them over the wrong drop-zone.

A couple of hours later saw Tom going home with his car on the back of a breakdown truck and the soldiers marching over the horizon back to base.

Tumbleweed

Caroline Atterwill

———

Tumbleweed – what a whimsical word when reading it on its own.
But it seems quite apt for my life
and a word I'd never associated with it before.
Rolling throughout the town, year after year,
with no point or purpose.
If it's in the way, you kick it.
If it rolls through your door, you expel it.
In fact, you only really take notice when it is a nuisance
or a hindrance because, let's face it,
it's not pretty enough to enhance your home in a vase
or clean enough to be associated with or to be around.
When the wind blows, people move.
When the dust enters your eyes, you cry,
and on the rare occasions that they grow,
people just close the doors behind it.
Out of sight, out of mind.

Look Before You Leap

Ambrose Doherty

———

Memories of times gone by, and those no doubt yet to appear, when a foolish act committed with all good intention, with no harm meant, has left me at my wit's end.

My usual reaction to these sudden and unfortunate happenstances is to run and hide. That, however, is just to compound the problem. Honesty dictates that apologies where appropriate are warranted. Moreover, a quicker witted approach would have sufficed.

The secret after much soul-searching is to look before you leap, think before you act and to keep one's wits about you.

If it were that simple – and for most it is. I'm tired of repeatedly putting my size tens in my mouth.

'One Over the Eight'

Caroline Atterwill

———

I've never come across this saying before, which is quite unusual considering on more than one occasion people looking at me might have thought I was "one over the eight."

I've been drunk, pissed, off my face, slurring, legless, spannered, and now, due to the fine work of the English language, I've also been one over the eight.

Fly Off The Handle

Kelvin Thompson

———

I fly off the handle every day,
Especially when things don't go my way.
I hate getting up so I don't go to sleep,
I hate staying awake, I just moan and weep.
I hate eating food, it takes too long,
My time is more useful just singing a song.
I fly off the handle when the sun is hot,
But I fly off the handle when it's not.
I hate crossing the road so then I ride,
I hate getting to the other side.
I hate those who walk in front of me,
I hate those behind that I can't see.
I hate bikes, cars and buses too,
I hate those people who jump the queue.
I hate everybody excepting me,
I hate everything that is not free.
Some things really drive me round the bend,
Like writing this poem without an end.

When In Rome
Richard Baker

When in Rome   Michelangelo painted a dome
When in Rome   Barbarians seized the throne
When in Rome   enlightened Englishmen took artefacts home
When in Rome   gladiators killed for fame
When in Rome   popes made infallibility claims
When in Rome   sanitation came with drains
When in Rome   St Paul was locked in chains
When in Rome   driving slow brings no gains
When in Rome   early Christians suffered many pains

Bugger Rome   I think I'll stay at home

The Early Bird Catches The Worm
Kelvin Thompson

———

The bird starts early this morning
in the fresh early dew.
It was as the day was dawning
and everything was new.
To get the fresh bread from the shop,
being the first in line,
I got the bus and sat on top,
better than being behind.
Because I am an early bird
I have all day to find
some things that others find absurd.
You lose if you're behind.
An early bird catches the food
because it got there first.
An early bird has a good mood
as it sits upon its perch.
It's good to get there first in life
in whatever thing you do.
There is no conflict and no strife
and great satisfaction too.

The Early Bird Catches The Worm

Carl Williams

———

The man woke up early to try to get the best spot on the wall as he might get landed with a tiny area to paint his rather large design, which would land him in quite a predicament, and with a large prize at stake he needs to do everything in his power to get him on the winner's spot as this could change his life. He could finally pay a deposit on somewhere to live. This could be the chance he needs to be normal and live like a human, not like an animal in the gutter on the streets.

So he knows he had to get there first to be in with a chance and this is more important for him than any other artist coming to win the prize. It's also a chance for him to prove he still is the man he used to be and can be, and get some respect back. Everybody knows he had it, so did he, but does he still have it? There is only one way to find out. Get there early and do your best. Bring his self out of himself! And smash it!!!

J-J-J-Jolly Jack Tars
Richard JJJJJJJones

————

The ship jigsawed left and right, jay-walking across the ocean. Not because the rudder was jaded, but because two of the three pirates aboard were arguing over which channel at the junction of the approaching islands they should take.

It had started when Jack Russell – who had a real Jekyll and Hyde personality – had "accidentally" hit Joe Bloggs in the face with a block and tackle, and the fact that Joe had a glass jaw really didn't help.

Joe believed it was because Jack was jealous of Joe's pet jackdaw, and Jack couldn't catch one himself. That led to Joe giving Jack's favourite jacket away to a jumble sale.

Things were then made worse when, whilst on a hunting trip on a Caribbean island, the "car" Jack had hired for the three of them turned out to be a real jalopy.

So now the ship was in jeopardy, with the constant jerky movements.

John Bull, the third – and most jovial – of the pirate trio, was making the most of the otherwise empty small cabin, glad for once not to be jam-packed in, cheek-by-jowl, and was chilling-out to some jazz music whilst stuffing his face with a job-lot of junk food, and smoking a joint.

Hearing jagged snippets of the argument from up on deck, John had decided that the ship was jinxed. Either that or it was some kind of poetic justice that was playing out from the time when both Jack and Joe had used John's jodhpurs as a make-shift fishing net, totally ruining them in the process. Whatever the case, John had decided to let them stew in their own juices for a while.

But then, on a snap-judgement, John – having been quite a Jack-the-lad in his youth, and as a Jack- of-all-trades – decided instead to play a juvenile joke on his ship-mates, one he had learned from his time owning and running a sandwich shop, which had been his attempt at keeping up with the Joneses down the road from where he had grown up.

The result of this was that Jack and Joe eagerly munched-down on some expertly made sarnies as John spouted various amounts of culinary jargon in his efforts to distract Jack and Joe from the fact that the sandwiches were stuffed full of extra hot jalapeños.

That certainly quietened things down a bit for the most part, for quite a while. The only sounds for the rest of the day – and well into the night – coming from the old-fashioned toilets, which were clearly struggling with the demands being made of them.

Once recovered, Jack and Joe figured that some pay-back was in order, and that they'd go for the jugular.

Having raided the old ornate jewellery box that was now acting as a kind-of medicine cabinet, Jack and Joe drugged John's drink with a load of sleeping pills.

Later, when John finally came around, he discovered that he was tied to the mast. However, that wasn't the worst of it.

In his efforts to release himself, John released a spring mechanism, which shot him up the mast as though jet-propelled, like an over-sized Jack-in-the-box, leaving him floating in the breeze in place of the Jolly-Roger.

The bang as the trap's counter-weight hit the deck caused Joe to cry-out "JEEPERS CREEPERS!" as Jack merely muttered to himself "Jam tomorrow, jam yesterday, but never jam today."

A Rhyme Based On Sayings About Plants

Kelvin Thompson

———

A rolling stone gathers no moss
The one wearing the hat is usually the boss
Can't see the wood because of the trees
Could smell the honey but can't see the bees

Great oaks from little acorns grow
But nature, you know, moves very slow
Put someone out to pasture because they are old
They may dig the garden and find gold

Letting the grass grow under your feet
Take the world as it is, sour or sweet
The grass is always greener on the other side
The bus is always full when you're waiting for a ride.

Resting On One's Laurels

Peta Trigger

———

Before I came here, I was resting on my laurels. I was just drifting from day to day without conscious purpose. Before, I was studying and writing but I became indolent, getting into bad habits of sloth and ennui.

One day, having passed and re-passed it many times, I went into the Jesus Centre. From that point on, my lazy life took on a new, active aspect. It was the Jesus Centre that told me about Hope and after only a few weeks, I have turned my life around – in terms of activity, going from strength to strength, attending classes like this one, learning new things and discovering abilities I thought I never had.

To Singe One's Wings

Richard Jones

———

Another day in the workshop and Talus was just putting the final strokes to his latest blueprint for a new, radical device. Upon finishing, Talus decided to take the rest of the day off and, with an adequately filled coin-purse, he set off for a gentle stroll down to the beach.

As usual, it was a lovely sunny day in Athens and Talus had decided to treat himself to a wine-skin of top quality spiced wine and a good selection of sweet-meat treats to wash down. Having found a comfortable spot, Talus settled down and was soon asleep. But not for long.

As the sun was reaching for the horizon, Talus woke up, hearing an odd mix of excessively loud seagulls and laughter. Looking along the beach, he saw an unusual figure shambling towards him, heading for the path leading back into town. Talus felt he recognised the stranger and as the man got closer he realised that it was his old boss, Daedalus, albeit older and somewhat haggard looking, but weirdly covered in a mix of wax and feathers.

Although still angry at Daedalus, Talus couldn't think of anything else to say other than, "Where the tartanus have you been?" to which Daedalus wearily replied, "Don't ask!"

Imagination

I Scream

Caroline Atterwill

———

Session 99
99= Ice cream
Ice cream = ?
I Scream
Why?
I scream.
Why?
Because for the last ninety nine fortnights
I've had to drag myself out of bed,
eyes closed, dry mouth,
dreading the next few hours.
Voluntary, they said.
Voluntary, my arse!
Mandatory more like.
And then crawling to the bus at ten in the morning
whatever the weather.
Cold, usually.   Raining mostly.
Snowing – yeh, a lot of the time.
Sun, very rare. Heat, very rare.
On the bus, cussing, falling asleep,
having to shake my head to wake.
Now –
Creative Writing,
here we come.

Getting off the bus, thinking of all the excuses I could have made
not to be here in the first place,
But here I am, walking towards Oasis.
Here I am.
For the next hour I'll be digging out of my brain
such ideas and memories
that have never come before
and on paper they are written.

The Magic Box
(Based on the poem 'The Magic Box' by Kit Wright)
Ambrose Doherty

———

I will put in the box
the earliest memories of being,
from my tears at the birth of first child
to the paperwork needing to be filed.
I will put in my box
my astonishment, my joy and my hope,
a train set named Thomas and Friends,
the promise I made at the start.

I will put in the box
gladly so, my disappointment in self soon to show,
my heart that was broken just then
and the scale that marked out of ten.

My box is made from despair,
in combination with hope never lost
that some day a solution be found.

I will work on my box to improve,
no more sorrow to endure ever more,
my eternal love for my first one
and hope of forgiveness one day.

My Magic Box
(Based on the poem 'The Magic Box' by Kit Wright)
Caroline Atterwill

I will put in the box
the final iced breath of winter
the first taste of strawberries in summer
the smell of risen baked bread.

I will put in the box
the vibration of a bee's wings
a headache from the night before
the sound of the first tear of heartbreak.

My box is made from tears and despair
with the last shine of the sun creeping round the corners,
with diamond encrusted plasters bringing it all together.

I shall sit in my box
as a padded cell
and use the movement of my arms as colours of rainbows
to turn white into life.

The Magic Box
(Based on the poem 'The Magic Box' by Kit Wright)
Richard Cotton

———

I will put in the box
the trail of a slimy snail,
coal from the land of the green dragon
a tooth of a mermaid, all shiny smooth like a gem.

I will put in the box
a first fierce chilli from lands far away,
the jeans of a laid-back jailbird,
a cockatrice from a mysterious place.

I will put in the box
a jam jar full of fireflies,
the juice of a freshly squeezed lemon, ripe from the tree,
a roar from a lion pulled from the mouth with magical glee.

My box is fashioned from moonstones and pearls
with pentagrams on the corners.
Its hinges are skeletal bones, fingers gripping tight.

I shall fly my box across the bright blue sky of the Pacific winds
then land upon green lands the colour of peas.
having to shake my head to wake.

My Magic Box
(Based on the poem 'The Magic Box' by Kit Wright)
Richard Jones

———

I will put in the box
the flash of a flaming match when struck,
the foundation of a towering edifice,
a fountain of frolicking faeries.

I will put in the box
a magic wand made of multicoloured light,
a mysterious yet mighty minotaur,
a marvellous and magnificent mega-yacht on a sea of dreams.

My box is made of dragon-fire tipped with starlight
with unending circles covering every inch
and a lock made of mithril and diamonds.

I can hide in my box when the world is too big.
I can keep safe all that is precious to me.
No-one and nothing can break into it.
Inside it, all is protected, even from time itself.

Foraging Gone Wrong

Richard Jones

———

WOW!!! This is GREAT!
    What are these things? I've never seen green mice before, or purple voles, for that matter.
Must remember where I found them 'cause them ain't ordinary mushrooms.
Hell, I only ate them 'cause I was hungry.
Why are the stars moving about?
And why is my barn lying on its side?
Whoa! My wings! I can't feel them.
Flying, spinning, swooping, BANG!!
Who put that wall there?
And who covered it in grass?
The floor?
What's that doing sideways?
I'm falling, falling into the sky!!!
Wait! I'm flying again.
Mmmmmm, a turquoise rabbit. Looks tasty.
(Yawn)
Oh, I'm tired – think I'll have a nap.
BANG!!! Damn it! Guess I should have landed first.
Ah, sleep. Just in time for daytime.
(The tractor he landed on starts up.)

Story

Story
Richard Baker

———

Is the story in the mind?
Yes, to begin with,
But, when read, for the reader the story is a solid entity.
It is paper and ink made solid.
Yet which is more solid, the thought or the parchment?
Is this debate irrelevant? Are both as important?
Can one exist without the other?

Many stories have existed over many millennia.
Many stories have been lost through lack of telling,
or do they reappear in another mind,
at a later time in a newer guise,
until the paper and ink restore them to immortality?

Perhaps the story can live alone
but when married to writing material, they truly exist for ever.
As long as people read them.

The Lake

Richard Jones

———

There was an old man who loved fishing and one day he took his grandson with him. There were three lakes where he would go but he would only go fishing in two of them. The day he took his grandson however, they visited all three.

At the first one they both caught a few small fish. At the second, they caught a couple of larger ones.

But when they got to the third one, the old man said, "In this lake is the biggest fish of all. It is so big it can break the line so we only try to catch it once and then let it go so other anglers can try to catch it."

"I caught it when I was a young lad, so now it's your turn and I'm going to rest under the trees."

For years this went on and when the old man passed, the boy kept fishing there.

Eventually one day, having grown into a young man, he bumped into a groundskeeper and asked about the fish in the third lake only to be told, "Sorry mate, there've never been any fish in that lake."

Over time, the young man grew old and became a granddad himself, and one day he took his grandson fishing.

The Selkie Wife

Caroline Atterwill

———

As the selkies finished their meal, they sat as they did every night around the coral where they slept and the elder of the group told stories of old!

There was a legend many years ago that seven of our kind emerged from the sea and washed up on the sand. They shed their skins for a short time so the elements of the new world would not destroy them, and to celebrate the coming to this new land, they started to sing and dance. But from nowhere a man appeared, stole one of the skins and ran, knowing that without her skin she could not return to her sea life.

As she chased him, he stopped, turned around and told her that she now belonged to him but promised after seven years he would return the skin and set her free. And his slave she became and he made sure all his needs were met. Not just the housework, cooking, cleaning and even helping him set up his boat in the morning and collecting the catch at night. And, of course, sex. But with her beauty fading and her health weak, when she fell pregnant it was traumatising. Whilst struggling to carry on her duties in her home, her pregnancy became harder and harder.

After nine months, she gave birth to a beautiful baby boy, and still whilst nursing her son and still a slave stuck on another world, all she could do was to wait, and wait she did. Then exactly seven years later, she came to him, exhausted, her beauty almost gone. She was quite unrecognisable from the lady he took many years before. Begging for her old life back, he just laughed in her face.

"You're mine now. When are you gonna accept that? "

"NEVER," was her reply and grabbing her son and skin, she ran, ran as fast as her legs would carry her.

But what about her young son, half of this world and half of the next? Her poor beautiful boy didn't fit in anywhere. She tried desperately for her family to accept him but he wasn't pure, so he was banished back to the land. She was distraught, her heart broken beyond repair. Her family tried to help her move on, without success, even tried to give her a partner, but her loss was just too much and engulfed her whole life. Well, how could her family expect her to forget the beautiful boy they made her leave behind? Her loss was all-consuming, and with her fading health and a broken heart, she wandered off in the middle of the night after two years of mourning and went to find her son. She managed to get to shore but was too weak by then, so, curling up on the sand, there she lay and there she died.

And it is said that on the sea shore every seven years, you can hear a howling like never heard before, the pain in her voice recognisable as a mother who lost her innocence, freedom and child. Such losses broke her and destroyed her health and eventually the pain overwhelmed her until her body and soul just withered away and died.

They Came Upon The Cave
Dee Linaken

———

They came upon the cave, a cavernous place with strange fences set up partitioning bits of it off and an overwhelming smell of goats. They also saw a fireplace, a large burnt area with rocks all around it.

That is when they saw gourds of milk and cheese which they started to eat, convincing themselves that it was alright because they had brought gifts to barter. Then suddenly sheep and goats started pouring in, herding themselves into the various pens.

The men stood up intending to show themselves when the light from the outside dimmed dramatically. A huge form filled the entrance, a giant of a man. They were filled with fear and while he had his back turned, pulling a huge boulder to cover the entrance, the men and Odysseus hid, terrified and trembling, deep in the cave, behind some rocks.

The Blinding Fury Of The Cyclops
Richard Jones

———

The pain! The pain! It's blinding, literally!
I'll kill them! I'll kill them all!
Rock, rock, nothing but rock!
Where are they?
They can't escape!
I'll kill them for blinding me!
Ouch!
They are putting rocks in front of me to try to trip me up!
They must be!
There wasn't a rock on the floor there before!
I can't see them!
If only I could see to find and crush them!!
I'll smash them to dust!!!
No! No! I can't find them!
They must still be here somewhere!!!

Herla's Hope

Richard Jones

———

In the folk story "King Herla's Ride," Herla spends three nights underground with the King of the Hollow Hills but on returning to his land finds two centuries have past. He is destined to ride along the borders of Wales and England until he finds his own time.

It's all gone. My home isn't even a ruin but a series of dents in the ground. My people are no longer my own, my kingdom has long since been mine to rule, my wife is nought but dust. What is there left for me? I have seen so much over the years. Too much. The madness of man has overcome my land so many times but still time has plodded onwards, ever onwards. I still don't know how a few nights could become a few centuries, but more painful still has been the lonely ride down the millennium, searching for a way back. There must be one! A river only ever flows downstream but I have seen mechanisms that can defy this, so I must believe the same must be possible with time.

The King of the Hollow Hills had much he cared about, even loved, so he must at least be able to imagine losing it all and therefore would not be so heartless as to trick me into losing everything without some way of getting it back.

So on I ride, hoping against hope that I will find a way back, but as each day becomes a month, a year, a century, I feel that I should just jump down from my horse and become dust . But what if I just ride that little bit longer?

Cider Story
Richard Baker

———

On a steamy Midsummer's morn, the sun brought in the dawn. Two drunken peasant farmhands supped their cider flagons. Drunk they were, happy drunk, joyful drunk, the many pints of cider making their minds dance. Such sweet, sweet, strong, strong cider. No better way to spend a hot steamy Midsummer morn.

In a happy haze they dozed, slumbered on the carpet of warm grass, early bees a-buzzing for their nectar. Two peasant farmers just as buzzing with their own nectar.

After a short while, they spied an old friend a-wandering their way. He was not buzzing like them. He looked miserable and sullen, dark and moody, sad and lonely. He begged to join in their cider drinking and they asked why he had no cider of his own as last year's apple harvest had been so plentiful. He took a drink and then explained his unhappy plight.

Eighteen months previous, on New Year's Day, the apple god he forgot to pay. For all knew well if they didn't feed the apple trees with bread and cider while a-wassailing on winter's deep cold morn, you would not drink on warm Midsummer dawn the sweet fruits from the apple god's abundant summer store.

Oasis And Hope
(Written in 2015)
Caroline Atterwill

———

O asis and Hope were two powerful wizards, Oasis being a cruel and ruthless man who had no pity for anyone and who crushed anyone who came in his path, whilst Hope was a white wizard, pure of heart and protector of all. Centuries ago, there was a fight, good against evil, for control of the earth, and after many years and thousands dead, they came to an agreement that Oasis would rule half the world and Hope the other half.

Hope thought that things were finally sorted but that wasn't what Oasis thought and he wanted control of the entire world. Where Oasis ruled was dark, dismal and dying and Hope would never relinquish his beautiful, bright, healthy and magical world to his enemy.

For years Oasis tried everything to gain control of Hope's empire but, with the help of his magical cane, he was able to create a force field to keep all that was evil out. So the only way Oasis could beat Hope and not only gain his empire but also his powers, was to steal his cane. He wandered across the land kidnapping the innocent and pure to get past the force field and into Hope's castle, which he successfully did.

So once again, after many a year, they were face to face and ready to battle. Both sides, good and evil, spent weeks battling each other with blood spilt and hundreds dead. It finally came down to Oasis and Hope and they fought, bolts of light thrown and magical spells cast. Oasis knew that without the cane he would never win but one of the bolts was just too quick for Hope and he went down. As Oasis stood over Hope, he took the cane out of his hand and finally in that second all his dreams and wishes had come true.

But then something strange started happening. As all Hope's power entered Oasis' body, all the goodness in his heart, as well as all the magic, did too. As the powers fought inside Oasis, the new powers of Hope were too much to handle in the black hearted man and within seconds of holding the cane, he was consumed by powers he couldn't control and his face started to melt and he exploded. Hope eventually put the world back to the heavenly place it once was, and good, as always, conquered evil.

Escape

Caroline Atterwill

———

As he squeezed through the small gap he had made in the iron gate, all that was on his mind was freedom. He had been locked up in this institution, like a dog, since when? He couldn't quite remember.

And the reason? Being just that little bit different to most other people.

But now, after months of planning, with his cross round his neck, he had made it through the castle's many corridors and staircases, and finally he was out. So, quick on his feet, he ran down the dark, dark pathway and through the woods and when the stitches in his side were too much to bear, he slowed down and decided to rest for a while.

As he looked around the forest he came upon a broken mirror and as he went closer, he saw to his horror that his chain and cross were no longer around his neck. He must have lost them during the escape. As he looked into the mirror, he tried to understand the reasoning for his incarceration. Okay, he was smaller than most and yes, his ears were a little bit on the pointy side, but apart from that, he didn't see any other reason why they would hold him there.

Tired and hungry, he looked up at the stars and noticed that this night there appeared a full moon. He smiled, trying to think of the last time he had seen one, but this train of thought was interrupted by the pain he was beginning to feel. His muscles started to stretch and his bones distorted and fractured. The agony was unbearable and he didn't understand what was happening to him. Well, why would he? He had been so drugged up whilst locked in the castle that his state of mind had been altered, and apparently that wasn't all that had been. Looking up at the moon, he howled uncontrollably. And all became clear.

I Had To Take A Walk

Richard Jones

———

I had to take a walk. Just needed to get away from things for a bit. A gentle stroll along the old river usually helped to clear my head. This time, with so much on my mind, I walked further than I ever had before. By late evening I came across an old tree that was leaning out over the water. It was so odd that I stopped and just stared at it for a while. Eventually I decided to sit down and take a rest. As I watched the water slowly drift past, I heard a faint voice.

"Jump."

I looked around but saw no-one. Moments later it came back, a bit louder.

"Jump in."

I got up quickly but a short search again revealed no-one. Then a spindly branch suddenly moved on the periphery of my vision, and from the same direction came again…

"Jump in!"

Alarmed now, I shot to my feet and slowly, quietly, walked right up to the odd tree. After walking around it a couple of times, I called out in a loud whisper "Hello?" before cautiously taking a few steps towards it, until I was close enough to be able to reach out and touch its bark, that appeared to be dead and exceptionally rough-looking. Then, just above a whisper, I said "Who's there?"

Almost immediately, I was answered by a gentle yet sinister chuckling, the sound now seeming to emanate both from the odd tree and from inside my head. I started to warily back away from this increasingly foreboding arboreal creature. On the third step a small twig broke off and splashed into the river, re-directing my attention back to the running water that was now murky and was itself exuding some form of menace.

The voice spoke again, this time more forcefully.

"Jump in!"

Genuine fear began to envelope me when............**SNAP!!!**

A fairly large branch, still attached by a thread, swung down. I dived, twisted and rolled, ending up in a heap on the river-bank. The branch had still managed to catch me, cutting my arm, but had it not been for my heightened alertness I would've ended up in the river, and the spot where I would've landed was now beginning to bubble and foam - as if I *had* fallen in.

Again, the voice spoke. Although not shouting, any restraint, any desire for quietness was now gone. Distorted as it over-lapped itself, in an increasingly demonic tone, it kept repeating the words "Jump in", goading me, daring me to heed its command. But at the same time it was chuckling again, the chuckle occasionally turning into a malevolent belly-laugh.

Whether by the sudden gathering of clouds or by my imagination I couldn't tell, but the dim light began to darken, and as fear tightened its grip on me, my only remaining thought was to get away as quickly as possible. Scrambling to my feet I set off at a run, going as fast as I dared, being so close to the river.

As the odd tree was left further and further behind, rooted to its spot, the talking voice joined the other in its menacing mirth before other voices that were in fact just that one voice multiplied, contributed to the clamour, until it was impossible to distinguish just one bout of laughter.

As I ran, the sound seemingly coming from the tree faded until the noise was just in my head, then that slowly faded too.

By the time I got home, I had managed to mostly compose myself, though the shiver that periodically went up my spine would continue for most of the night.

The next morning, in the cold light of day, the world seemed normal, as though nothing had ever happened. Though it wasn't until nearly a week later, after a report in the newspaper of a death at that exact spot, did I begin to research the area, and my investigations revealed the tragic history of what was once known as "The Salient of Suicides," a tide of tragedies spanning centuries.

The biggest shock, however, was yet to come. For, when the police investigation into this latest fatality concluded a case of "accidental death", the name of the unfortunate soul was finally revealed.

It was ....

The Broken Sword

Richard Jones

———

It is 2117.
The world is in a mess
that not even the most blind optimist can see a way out of.
In the British Isles, things are as bad as ever.
Pockets of law and order remain in the last outposts of the royal family.
The rest of the nation is in anarchy.
Gang leaders rule like warlords.
Then a discovery is made.
Eddie Mordred, having been run out of his home,
finds an old cavern where he takes refuge,
and in the depths unearths a shattered blade.
A blade that is later revealed as Calibur, the predecessor of Excalibur.
Thus begins a journey to find the legendary sword.
A journey to save the ancient lands of Britannia,
And, perhaps, the rest of the world.

Creatures

Zoo Visits

Ambrose Doherty

———

Oh my Lord, it's Monday again, oh so soon. How does it come round so quickly? If only the herd were aware of how much this gets my goat, and that's not the one I've been promised for lunch. I'd better behave this morning, 'cos I really like goat!

Gates are open, here they come. If only they knew! Mondays, what is it about the Japanese on Mondays, do they have some connection to Mondays? Is it spiritual or emotional, or do I just enjoy having my picture taken? I don't know.

Now don't tell fibs, you know, my boy. Should you let them know? Well, you will soon enough. Save it, it'll be more fun, not just for them. Patience is a virtue after all. Ha ha. Wait for it!

Trickle, trickle, in they stroll, past all the others, their cameras aglow.

The meerkats are lively this morning, well when are they not? How long have I got? Meerkats to me, about twenty, maybe thirty minutes. Good!

Right, first things first. Get those indoors in order, a look should suffice. They know the routine.

Settle yourself, Ambrose, on your throne that they built, motion controlled, the great orange stare to unleash. I'd love to warn them with a roar through their souls, but it would ruin the fun and what good is that? Save it, it'll be worth it. Wait a minute, Ambrose, you did this the same way last Monday. Are you losing your edge? Nah, if it ain't broke, don't fix it.

Attention now, minutes to go, patience, patience, timing is of the essence.

Closer, closer – you've done it enough times.

Wait......wait.........cameras aloft...timing,son....timing...... NOW!!!

Once again,

Tiger, Tiger, burning bright!!!

From A Spider Dating Web Site
Caroline Atterwill

———

I'm very furry and love nights in the nest snuggling with my legs wrapped around you. I'm looking for a male. Looks not important, intelligence not important, age not important, as long as you are able to stay for dinner.

In Memory Of Hoddy
Claire

———

I am going to write about Hoddy, a very special cat. He appeared to be part feline, part human and was a much loved member of our family. He had a sad start to his life. We found him as a little, emaciated, abandoned stray, surviving on whatever scraps came his way.

He was timid at first when we took him home, and shied away from all our fuss, but it wasn't long before he gained our trust and soon became the boss of us! Essentially a street cat, he soon became used to good food to eat, but still liked to earn his keep by bringing home the odd mouse for a treat.

Over the years he established his position as Alpha male, became a loving companion to my son Jake. He tolerated the arrival of two young kittens to our family and still remained top dog.

He lived a long and happy life and passed away peacefully at a ripe old age. He is laid to rest at the bottom of our garden, wrapped in my son's favourite blanket, which he liked best.

Princess

Caroline Atterwill

———

Princess was my first ever pet, my pet rat. Before her I had huge dislike of all things rodent-y, hamsters, guinea pigs, gerbils, etc, but this was only because I had heard terrible stories about them, the biting, the scratching, the scavenging stories that most people would have heard, but my preconception was wrong, as I found out when I was holding my beautiful Princess. Then my home became her home, and we did nearly everything together.

She would take food from my lips, settle down on a night sitting round my neck, and she even came to the shops with me, the sign being her tail which was visible on my neck. She seemed to sense when I was okay. She was a great companion, my beautiful Princess. But after about three years the inevitable happened.

One morning my partner woke up and like any other proceeded to make us both a coffee and then went into the living room. Within seconds he rushed back into the bedroom and gave me the bad news and of course I cried. When asked what I wanted to do with her lifeless body, I asked my partner to dig a hole in the back garden and rest her there, so I got a box and layered it with sawdust because I couldn't bear the thought of her being uncomfortable and cold. And there she rested, or so I thought until an argument arose one day, totally unrelated to Princess, and like in most arguments, things are said to hurt. And out of the blue he blurted it out.

"And you know your precious Princess, well she isn't comfortably buried in your nice little box. Like I'd bother for a rat."

So I asked, "So what did you do with her?" , his response being, "Well, I took her out of the box, put her in a plastic bag and threw her in the bin." I was mortified. How could he do such a cruel and terrible thing to a creature that meant so much to me? I didn't understand it. Just pure viciousness of a cold hearted man.

Ants

Peta Trigger

———

Ants, in the summer, are the bane of my life. (Perhaps I exaggerate.) They happen every year, beginning directly outside my front door. The first I know of their presence is the sawdust just under the door in my porch, inside the house. They chew their way through the doorstep and the door frame.

They have already appeared this year, as a repeat of this time last year. So I dived for the Dermis ant powder insecticide and doused the area immediately below the door, inside and out. But this is only a temporary expedient because a plague of ants breaks out in myriad areas all over the brick drive leading down to the street door. In fact, I have my work cut out in keeping them from invading the house – and only by doing their individual nests with powder on a daily basis. I think life would be more pleasant without the little beasts, but I suppose God created ants for a purpose!

My Least Favourite Creature

Richard Jones

———

Wasps, damned wasps. God's worst design for a creature. They have no use ; bees at least make honey. They are a plague on picnics, annoying on the beach, a nightmare in country parks. They won't leave you alone. You try various tricks to keep them away, keeping a swatter close at hand. There are many dangerous animals in the world, but I think few are so universally loathed as wasps. The world would genuinely be a better place if they didn't exist. Wasps, damned wasps.

A View From Eden

Richard Baker

———

My names are many! Sometimes Satan, others, the Devil. For today's story I shall call myself Snake.

Your first hearing of me will be under this name in schoolroom or church room or bedroom, but this first story will be told you by others so let me tell you first hand from my point of view.

On the day I crept into God's garden and saw God's creatures Adam and Eve, I wondered what the almighty fool was up to. He had created two wonderfully formed, beautiful models, then planted them in the garden like two useless wall plants or mindless insects. Those creatures were perfection except for one or two things. First, they didn't realise their beauty, or each other's. Secondly, these perfect creatures were a limited edition of two. Being an entrepreneur, I naturally taught them mass production.

My lesson must have been a good one. You see, for the expenditure of just one apple, the production line comes down to you…and many millions more forever and ever to damnation's end.

Thank you all. Now just go forth and multiply.

Food and Drink

The Cook Up
Richard Jones

———

Terry was in a pickle. Mandy had spilt the beans on their up-to-now secret relationship. He had also been seeing Beverley on the quiet and although she was a salt of the earth type of person, Terry was left feeling unfulfilled and so had pursued Mandy.

Terry's good mate Jerry had warned him that his half-baked idea to see two women at once would cause problems and that he could find his goose well and truly cooked in the end. Upon learning of Mandy's revelation, Beverley went bananas and stormed up to Terry, properly cheesed off. Seeing her expression, Terry knew he would have to eat humble pie.

"You think you're the big cheese, the cream of the crop," she yelled. "Well you've just bitten off more than you can chew." And with that, she stormed off.

With his feelings as flat as a pancake and stewing in his own juice, Terry decided he would explain everything to Mandy and, walking on eggshells, he told her the whole sorry story. Unfortunately, Terry didn't know Mandy as well as he thought he did and soon discovered that Mandy was as nutty as a fruitcake. He found Beverley had already told Mandy everything and she had then immediately proceeded to make mincemeat out of Terry's stamp collection. With that done, Mandy then dropped Terry like a hot potato.

Later, in the pub, whilst chewing the fat with Jerry, Terry decided that you really couldn't have your cake and eat it.

Fire
Matthew

I am a 26 year old man, my name is Matthew. My living circumstances are very poor. I can't cook on a cooker or a microwave so my experience of fire would be barbecuing, which I enjoy. I get to cook a variety of things, one of which is a big fat cheese burger with onions and cheese slices. There are other meals I prepare. These are not as tasty as my favourite though, the cheeseburger.

Anyway, the way I make my fire is I use firelighters then sticks on top. I start with small twigs which I break off a tree, then I pile them up to make a nice stack of twigs, then what I do is I get bigger twigs and do the same. I keep doing it until I have the biggest log on top of the rest. This is a perfectly built fire.

What I do after this is I build some bricks around it to keep it all together so it's strong and won't collapse or fall to bits. Lastly I put a grate on top and a saucepan. The fun bit comes next – the cooking. I use a lighter to ignite the fire and watch it burn. Finally I have made the perfect fire and can cook my dinner.

A Recipe

Ambrose Doherty

———

In the beginning there was a normal, somewhat common-place existence that pervaded life and as is the nature of the world, the solar system, and the universe all, the recipe changed.

Note to self: All measurements to be based upon a simple principle – use as much as necessary.

Throw together a quantity of unforeseen circumstance, accident, and ensuing struggle. Mix with ample quantities of woe and self pity.

Knead with vast amounts of unwanted sympathy and allow to rise disproportionately.

Add the spices liberally, commencing with the discovery that the physical will recover, not as before but close. Relief. (Short-lived, as the universal principle raises itself once more.)

The discovery that dessert remains, consisting of ingredients too numerous to mention. An Eton Mess of a sort.

Add them all at once into a blender and give it a rapid blitz.

The ensuing result is the recipe of Happenstance,

unavoidable but nonetheless real.

The recipe for the Perfect Storm.

Welcome to my world.

The Drinks Vending Machine
Adam Bowles

———

As a result of being part of the group of people classed as "long term unemployed," I have been placed on the work programme.

Ingeus offers a range of facilities such as computer access and free postage but at its heart is a vending machine. It sits beside the reception desk and dispenses mochas, espressos, cappuccinos and teas, all without charge.

So whether Big Jim is wanting to explain why an emergency of a medical nature had prevented his attendance at a mandatory session with his advisor or Shirley had popped in to explore Universal Match in her lunch hour, hoping to secure full time employment so that she can afford child care, or myself spending an hour prepping for the CRCS labourers' card exam, we are all drawn to the vending machine for free refreshment, perhaps standing closer to another human being and conversing more than we have done for a very long time.

Station Vending Machine
Richard Baker

———

Andy   late for school, no breakfast, rush and bustle, hair not combed, shirt untucked, a Mars bar for Andy.

Simon   suit pressed, tie straight, white shirt shining, early for the office, maybe a bottle of orange juice for Simon.

Angela   British Transport police officer, exhausted after an eight hour shift, a packet of crisps before a good day's sleep.

Brian   trainspotter, another day at the station, one of everything from the vending machine.

David   homeless and penniless, would, like Brian, like everything from the machine but can have nothing but a longing glance.

Vending machine empty, like David but, unlike David, a pouch full of coins.

Daniel   vending machine owner, sits in his Mayfair office with best Colombian coffee, full butter croissant and freshly squeezed orange juice,

Would never use one of those damned machines, too expensive.

In Costa

Caroline Atterwill

———

Towering like high rises, a family of paper cups stands to attention, waiting for their fifteen minutes of fame.

The smell of coffee infuses the air and with a whoosh, clang, the odd hiss and bubbling in the background, the rotating cogs and wheels work in harmony, like a single entity.

Just An Average Thursday!

Ambrose Doherty

———

The aroma, the convulsion of a myriad of sound,
  musical, vocal, mechanical,
outside, inside,
all encompassing, or so it appeared.
A cacophony of life for the experience of all present,
And yet somehow more so.
A focus difficult to define.
On show, all that humanity has to offer, in all its facets.
Facets – there's a beginning,
a word of such potential and of equal fear.
We all possess them, some on show
and others kept with deep and secret memories attached,
to be revealed only to those dear enough to confide in.
It's a wondrous realisation to embrace all these things simultaneously,
whilst sharing time together
within the confines of a simple coffee shop.
An experience indeed and as such one that would become
a pleasant memory of just an average Thursday morning.
I shall have to do this again some day.

Costa
Richard Cotton

———

The music played, with the mix of people talking. The smell of coffee wafted on the breeze as fans rattled in the ceiling. Some sat relaxed, drinking soft drinks, chatting idly about the day. Some smiled, others frowned. The sun shone warmly.

She walked through the door, pram first, a cardholder perched on the back.

He watched, wondering what was the next strange thing he would see. The poster "Spill the beans" fired his imagination. A story formed on the blank page in front of him.

Meeting the manager was a pleasure of its own. Each to their own, drawing a sense of time passing. Some would see it flash past, others would see it go slowly.

She sat outside, a puzzled look on her face at what was going on inside.

The air was calm and pleasant as he sat there writing with others of a creative kind. The experience as a whole was of a calm, peaceful day, which he hoped to carry with him through the rest of the week.

Taking in the ambience of the world, seeing new faces to place within stories and seeing if they would be evil or kind.

Large wall posters proclaimed what drinks there were to be had. The loud noise of machines broke into his world, making his ears hurt but wow, he would feel great for the rest of the day.

Café Of Dreams

Richard Jones

———

A nondescript day and light shone in a rather mundane way through the large window panes. At a table near one of the windows sat Toby Tichley, a rather nondescript man himself. He spent more time than not looking out of the window, watching the day and a myriad of people go by, with some of them entering the small café.

Toby would've sat right by the window but for the level of discomfort it would have caused. The last thing he wanted was to draw attention to himself, to be a kind of window display as though he were the star prize in the world's most disappointing game-show. He had just walked past a high-end supermarket lamenting the fact that most of the items in there were well out of his price range. Now, as he gingerly sipped his small coffee, trying to make his small slice of cake go as far as possible, Toby daydreamed. He was still sitting in the café but the circumstances of his life were quite different and continued to change as he dreamed.

No longer was his wallet a care home for elderly moths but contained a not insubstantial amount of money. More than enough to buy as many large coffees as he could drink in the next few hours, with appetisers, of course, the money having come from the relatively small but successful chocolate factory he owned, which he ran with humanity, unlike most other businesses.

As Toby day-dreamed, the sun temporarily ceased hiding behind the heavy cloud cover, bathing the world outside in a warm yellow glow, and Toby soon found himself imagining within his daydream the holiday he might soon take. Obviously it was somewhere warm and sunny and, within the confines of his mind, Toby had landed in a peaceful Middle East.

First he would wander around the ancient ruins of Petra, walk down the infamous Siddique towards the treasury buildings. With his curiosity satiated as much as possible, he would take to the deserts of Syria and explore the sites of Palmyra. That done, he would top things off by making an attempt himself – albeit a small one – to find the site of one of the Seven Wonders of the World, the one about which the least was known. The only one for which even the site of it remains a mystery – The Hanging Gardens of Babylon.

CRASH!!! Before Toby can begin to plan out his search for the fabled gardens, an over-laden tray is knocked off a table by a boisterous toddler, who had entered with his mother, unbeknownst to Toby whilst he was deep in the grips of his imagination.

The sun outside was still staying ahead of the clouds but had lost more than some of its brilliance. Unable to pick up his daydream again, Toby picked up a nearby newspaper instead, hoping to find a laugh or two in the agony aunt section. However, no sooner than he had turned to the right page there was a knock on the window near him. Looking up, Toby saw the face of his best mate Les Longshanks peering back at him. And so, at the motioning of Les, Toby left the table, instantly forgetting the newspaper sitting on it and went to see what his friend wanted.

Seconds later an elderly man had taken his place and was joined shortly after by his wife as Toby and Les headed off down the street.

Spill The Beans
Richard Cotton

———

The large open room hummed with electricity. Agent Romeo sat in the chair, the small table in front of him held his laptop and briefcase. Villeano stood across from him, his face was taut and sweat ran down from his forehead.

"Come on Mister Alan, you'll spill the beans sooner or later."

Romeo sat there thinking about how this had come about.

Earlier that day he had sat at this same table in the Costa Coffee shop. The table by the window, this was the prearranged drop off point. Romeo felt slightly uncomfortable in his suit, whilst others around him sat there wearing casual clothing, busy nattering about their day ahead.

Romeo placed his briefcase on to the tabletop to take out the laptop and smart phone. He noted that there was a message waiting for him. 'Have your cake and eat it,' a secret code telling him he had something to read later. This would have to wait.

"It's raining outside." Romeo looked up to the fair maiden, her auburn hair flowing down to her waist. "Yet it is dry in here," he replied.

The lady dropped an envelope in front of him. "There is the menu."

She turned to head back the way she came. Romeo felt a slight heat rise in his face. Was he blushing? The menu offered all the normal coffees that the shop could sell. He was sorting out what was on the menu when the older man came to the table.

"Do you need some cake?" It was Villeano, Romeo knew that by the tag that was pinned to his Costa t-shirt.

"If there is any."

"Which coffee do you want?"

"Err, such a big choice."

"Come on you'll spill the beans soon."

"Don't panic me."

"Americano or cappuccino?"

"Which would you chose?"

"The one you like the most."

"I'll have an Americano large, please."

Villeano turned and Romeo could see the logo on the back 'Costa welcomes all.' Romeo smiled as he returned to the laptop where he was looking at what items he needed to order to re-supply this café.

The Perils Of Being Over-Confident When Pissed
(A Karaoke Story)
Sean Nelson

———

"Go on! Go on! Milo, give it some welly!" the baying crowd yelled.

"What to request?" thought Milo. "Over the Rainbow? No, too schmaltzy. Angels – Robbie Williams? No, the bollocks have been sung out of that one."

As his glass was filled again, inspiration took its course. Recalling his lost love, indeed, his first love – with a revelatory exclamation, he shouted to the compere, "Crazy, Patsy Cline." "Okay, mate," the compere retorted.

Wistfully, the very tipsy Milo conjured up his first love, took himself to one side in his mind and counselled himself not to cry.

And so the song ensued with only a handful of people in the pub knowing poor Milo's plight. The rest, uninterested, carried on their drunken banter, oblivious to the pain-drenched rendition.

Always ended up the same – out of key, self-pitying. They had been there only too often before, with his maudlin story which they had all been through anyway.

Change (quite literally) the record!

Book Titles, Song Titles and Lyrics

The City Of Mirrors
Liam

———

I can see me in them all
But what will I do?
I can't find my way out,
But when I found myself, I found you.
You are my compass.
You are my ladder.
You are my friend.
You are my heart.
You are my salvation.

1983

Richard Jones

———

A certain year.
It was dark but it was warm, comfortable and safe.
True contentment.
A slow steady heartbeat in my ears but oblivious to the outside world and all its troubles.
Then, when the time was right, movement – pain, light so bright, although I was unable to say it.
I left my sanctuary feeling cold and vulnerable.
I cried at the misery I was feeling, at all these strange new sensations that would take years to even begin to understand.
So, with a cry, I said hello to the world.
Yes, it was 1983, and I was born.

Here I Am

Caroline Atterwill

———

Here I am, in the dark, all alone.
My mother is drinking.
Here I am, in the dark.
My nappy needs changing.
My father is shouting.

Here I am, in the dark.
The hunger hurts my tummy.
The pushing starts.

Here I am, in the dark,
with my bottle dry.
The screaming is now piercing.

Here I am, in the dark,
shaking, not knowing.
The sound of punching and smashing of glass.

Here I am, crying quietly.
Here I am.

Please someone notice
because
here I am.

Homeward Bound

Ambrose Doherty

———

"I'm sitting in the railway station with a ticket for my destination, mmm, mmm, On my tour on one night stands, my suitcase and guitar in hand, mmm, mmm."

Aged 19 and back-packing across the mighty U.S.A.

My mate Phil in tow, with adventures to be anticipated, with sights, sounds the accompaniment, and what a journey it became.

From starting point N.Y. to finishing point the Canadian Border Station on the West Coast, north of Seattle, Washington State and deportation. Happy days!

Upon arrival back in Blighty, the memories cascading of the three month adventure of a lifetime still shining in all, with the exception of my mother who eight months later received a bill from the U.S. Government for the cost of the deportation procedures and the long flight home.

To say she was less than amused would have made old Queen Vic chuckle.

But at least we were Homeward Bound, both safe and sound.

Little High, Little Low
Robert Billingham

———

Life has been really low the last hours, days, weeks, months and year that have gone by. Nothing seems to go my way. Luck is always down, nothing is straightforward, always a hitch involved. The less luck I have, the worse it gets. So my life is low and my highs I meet with my friend Mr Drugs. He makes me high and happy. He is such a good friend, I am addicted to him for life. Without him I would be so low.

He costs me a fortune. I lost my friends and family over him. He causes me heartache, misery, but he is the only one that makes me high when I am down and low. I don't want him in my life any more. I want my life back and my family. He is the devil and I fight him every minute, hour of the day. He always wins. But I have a surprise for him in store. My life will get better and healthier and back to my normal way of doing things without him.

My life drug free is in the starting blocks and I will win and he will be left behind, out of my life for good. His highs mean nothing to me now. Keeping him away gives me the natural high I need and the lows I am dealing with by my new ways of thinking and doing things. He is going and will be out of my life for good. That's the high I need to help me with the lows I get. I am opening my eyes to what is left in my life.

A Story Based On Song Titles From The Group Lindisfarne

Richard Jones

———

I woke up to a brand new day, probably a beautiful day, with a warm feeling. But stormy weather was on the way and there were no heroes who could stop it and when thunder broke out, I turned a deaf ear and thought to myself, "Is it really good to be here?" Then the clear white light streaked out across the sky and I remembered the words of Lady Eleanor, "Meet me on the corner." I dreamed of nights with her, walking through the fog on the Tyne.

So I downed a coffee that had the words "Wake up, little sister" written on the cup and checked the date on the cheap, Chinese-style calendar that said it was the day of the jackal. However, a mile down the road I realised that I'd forgotten to lock my front door and set off at a run for home. Unfortunately, I tripped over a misprinted George Orwell book entitled 1983 and fell into a flower stand, causing them to all fall down. Then I saw Uncle Sam standing over me, laughing, and I realised I was dreaming, which explained the nearby signpost stating one hundred miles to Liverpool.

A Clear White Light

Ambrose Doherty

———

He had just experienced one of the worst times in a long time, and it was lasting, dragging, towards making no sense at all. Nothing seemed the same any more. Darkness had descended.

Yet from somewhere, and he knew not where, dawned a beautiful day. The stormy weather was less so and a clear white light surfaced once again. The nights - no longer would he fear their disturbing cargo.

A warm feeling embraced him as the realisation that the answer he yearned for had not fallen on deaf ears, as he sat with pencil and paper in the company of friends.

Encounters

Meeting At The Bus Stop

Caroline Atterwill

———

I waited at the bus stop for a bus which was running late. When I had first turned up, I was the only one there but a couple of minutes went by and a young girl pushing a pushchair slowly walked up to the shelter, and I am one of those annoying people who can't help but have a look at the baby. That really cheers me up for the day.

So I had a glance in the pushchair and saw a newborn all snugged in and as an "Ah" came out of my mouth, the baby's head turned towards my direction. So, like many people, I started baby talking, all the usual stuff, "Hello, beautiful, aren't you gorgeous?" but as I was talking to this gorgeous baby boy I was noticing his glances in my direction were short and he looked a bit confused, with his blue eyes all round the place. Realising, of course, that at that age he wasn't able to focus yet I thought to myself, "This is where your story and exploring begins, my darling."

The Visit

Ambrose Doherty

———

More like a summons, that's what it felt like. Why are these invitations so matter of fact and informal? It's not like I haven't been asked to attend before.

All in attendance, likeable to a man, with my welfare to the fore. Why then does this trepidation, anxiety and dread always accompany the journey you make twice a month? Maybe this will be different and the news equally so. Don't hold your breath, son.

Arrival brings feelings unwarranted, fear starts to grow. Best to get it over with and then home you can go.

"Hello Ambrose," his usual opening.

I wish he'd phrase it differently for once, to change the pattern and tone of what is to come.

"Got the recent test results for you."

Heart starts to pound, breathing increases, nausea. Oh, how I hate the nausea.

Gone is all care of what he may say, as long as he tells me

I'll live another day!

Be Yourself; Everyone Else Is Taken
Richard Cotton

———

Francis Crick sat at his table looking at the paper work. There was something not working for him. He had scribbled over the formula three times and still something was missing. He looked around when there was a gust of wind behind him. There was no window there. There stood a blue box with "Police" in white letters. A thought came into mind and that was, "How did that get there?" The door opened. A tall gangly man came from within the box. "Hello, my good friend, I am the Doctor."

"Doctor who?"

"Yes, that is me."

He was closely followed by a redhead. "See, Amy, the source of all the data on D.N.A."

"Excuse me. I'm Francis Crick and I'm still working on that. There seems to be something wrong and I can't work out what yet."

"Let me have a look." The Doctor moved over to where Crick sat. "Odd, I didn't know that you knew The Master."

"Who's he when he is around?"

"Well looking at these, he has been trying to get your formula for ages."

"Why is that?"

"He is looking into changing the Human D.N.A. into something else. But what I say is, be yourself; everyone else is taken."

An Unusual Meeting

Richard Jones

———

It was a fairly quiet night in the pub and Wellingborough-born Thom Yorke was playing a solo set of Radiohead's greatest hits when in through the door came Des O'Connor. His nose wrinkling at the "music" in the room, Des walked over to the bar for a pint of local ale and a whisky chaser.

As he was on his eighth round, Des ruminated on how much Northampton had changed since first coming here as a boy during the war and he decided the only good thing to have changed since then was that he could now (and had for some time) been able to drink. Finally Des's annoyance at the live music became too much to bear and, tottering on his stool, he began to boo.

Annoyed at the interruption, Thom stopped suddenly and yelled, "What's your problem?" to which Des replied," Stop that noise and play some music." Riled, Thom retorted,"Shut up, you old has-been. Some people do still actually like my music." Undeterred, Des continued, "Yeah, SOME people. Even as an old joke I'm still more famous than you."

As the remark hit home, Thom decided to call it quits for his gig and, having hastily packed his gear away, quickly set about drinking for himself. Several pints of lager later, Thom carefully slid down the bar next to Des and quietly said, "Look, I'm really sorry for calling you a has-been. I just don't know what to say when someone boos me. Security usually keeps non-fans out of the building so it's never happened before."

Nearly comatose, Des replied, "Welcome to my world." Several drinks later, and with both on the verge of being hospitalised for alcoholic poisoning, Thom got out his music gear and finished the night by playing "Dick-a-dum-dum" and "I Pretend."

"Whispering" Bob Harris Meets Alan Moore
Ambrose Doherty

———

The day began pretty much as normal. Late again, mildly overslept, yet late nonetheless, again.

Something on today and memory's not what it used to be. Note to self – write it down or stop whispering. You can't even hear yourself most of the time. What chance does that give the rest of them?

Especially Alan Moore. A writer of sound repute. A fellow Northamptonshire man, and to talk not of these things but of his taste in music.

Where to begin? Check the researcher's findings. Some clue at least.

Read his latest work. Found it difficult yet somehow mesmeric.

No help yet. (Doorbell chimes.)

Hello, Mr Moore. Please come in.

Sunday Afternoon

Richard Baker

———

O n a sunny Sunday afternoon in the lovely spring of 1914, Edgar and Walter, after promenading around the bandstand in Abington Park separately, retired to the Abington Park Hotel for late afternoon tea. When they sat together at the only table available, they exchanged polite but not obvious courtesy, for, given the time, it was very unusual to see two very young, fit men, one white and the other black.

The start of their conversation was again polite but muted, with the usual type of ice breaking comment.

"And what do you do, Walter?" said Edgar, to which Walter replied, "Sir, I am a professional footballer with The Cobblers, just transferred from the mighty Spurs."

"Good Lord," replied Edgar, "but I am also a sportsman, but being a gentleman of good breeding, and white, I play the amateur game with the odd shaped ball."

After this first encounter, they became firm friends. Both joined the service of their country within eight months and both lost their lives in the mud of Flanders within one year of each other.

Edgar Mobbs received the Distinguished Service Order; Walter Tull was cited for gallantry and the campaign for his award of a Military Cross continues.

Something Precious
Caroline Atterwill

———

"Can I trust you to keep something precious for me?"
I heard a voice say.

"Who are you and, more to the point, where are you?"

"Up here," I heard the voice say.

Looking up, I saw a cat sitting in a tree, and, with a quizzical expression on my face, I started to look around to see who else was about.

"You got it right the first time," the cat piped up.

To my astonishment, it suddenly clicked that it was the cat who was talking to me. After my initial shock, I answered, "What was that? I didn't quite hear you?"

The cat repeated, "Can I trust you to keep something precious for me?"

Out of curiosity more than anything else, I said, "Sure, why not? What is it?"

As the cat moved over to one side, I saw a small kitten cowering behind it. "I have to go hunting for food to feed my kitten but I have no-one to take care of her in my absence."

With me still not understanding if it was reality or not, the cat climbed down the tree with the kitten in her mouth and gently placed it in my hand.

"Back soon," she said and off she wandered into the woods.

Time

Time–Less
Richard Baker

———

Time, existence's great enigma.
Pattern is all in nature and the universe
but Man's great problem is always time,
Man's inability to pin down its measure and its pattern.
For it has only Man's construction to bound its limits
and set its pace and rhythm.
Yes, Time does mock Man
in its elusiveness and guile.
Does Man tell the time
or does Time tell Man?

Would You Rather Have A Rewind Button In Your Life Or Have A Pause Button?

Ambrose Doherty

———

Rewind or Pause?
A question I've asked often times.
What's it about except regret and dismay?
Regret is for those that feel sorrow
and that's a place to be left for tomorrow.
Negates the question really, doesn't it?
Would I change it, would I leave it?
I choose not to ask, could I change? It is yet another task.
If I changed would it change me and do I want that?
Endless questions prevail.
Could I pause to consider the events at the time?
Would I do anything different?
By now, if I had, I would know.
Therein lies the answer
And the answer is NO !!

The Call

Richard Cotton

———

John was on the phone wondering how much longer he had to be sat waiting for a voice to speak to him. It had been five minutes already. All he wanted was the answer to one question. The leak had started two days ago but it wasn't coming from him.

Those people in the call centre must be on a tea break or having dinner. All he felt was a pain from the loud music that was being blasted in his ear.

Never again would he phone them up. No, he would rather walk to the offices and talk to them in person. John glanced at the clock. It was ten minutes and still no answer.

What's Gone Is Gone...Or Is It?
What Remains Remains...Or Does It?

Ambrose Doherty

———

Questions, questions all around, And seldom answers to be found.

When I find myself alone and contemplation pops in for a chin wag, I sometimes question all things past, present, future yet to discover.

Who was it who said, and I quote, "There is no present. There is no future. There is only the past, happening over and over again now." I wish it were me, alas not so.

In my recollections of five decades (and a bit) gone, and memories contained therein, my life, I've decided, to this point at least, is one colossal diaspora.

It's like my physical presence and my memory of all things to this point have decided to disperse from their centre to the farthest corners they can possibly find.

"In search of what ?" I ask myself constantly. Speculation on such matters I've found helps not.

I've decided that the search for answers is in, and of itself, the purpose of the journey. My quest.

Of The Ancient Tower
Richard Jones

———

B abel.
It was meant to be a tower of strength.

A timeless pillar of mankind.

The supreme effort of humanity to reach God, and stand equal to Him.

But mere mortals have no place at such heights, just as an ant has no place in the company of lions.

To show this, the tower was struck down and the people dispersed to all corners of the globe, to teach them their folly and their weaknesses that they had overlooked in their great endeavour.

However, humans are stubborn creatures and over time they began to form the patterns of civilisation that would eventually bring them back together, and once again begin their efforts of attaining perfection.

Rochester Castle - A Day Under Siege

Richard Jones

———

Morning: Hungry, haven't eaten for two days and that was some two-week old horse meat. King John's army still sits outside the walls and still no help has arrived. The baron tries to keep our spirits up but it is a losing battle. As futile, it seems, as our attempts to keep the king from gaining this castle. We all know that this fortress is the key, the gateway to the kingdom, but the question is how much longer can we hold out.

Midday: The last two hours the king's troops have been ferrying an awful lot of pigs around, far too many for all his men to eat. The baron came by my post and I'm sure he looked very worried, maybe even a bit frightened. I think whatever the king is planning to do with those pigs, it's going to be really bad for us.

Afternoon: The pigs are all gone, which is weird, and worryingly the king has moved his army and the camp even further away, although they were already well out of range of our archers. The baron's personal chaplain has just been round offering prayers and words of encouragement and hope.

Late afternoon: I've heard reports that there's smoke in the cellar. An old soldier told me that they had mined under us and set fire to the pigs to weaken the foundations. On the baron's orders we've all been pulled back from the walls and have gathered in the middle of the Great Hall.

Evening: Disaster! I will soon be departing this world. Hope is gone but we fight on. There is nothing else, nothing left to do. A whole corner of the keep is gone, fallen into the foundations, and has taken other parts of the castle with it. What is left of us now sit at the top of the rubble. There are too few of us left now and we are all too weak to fight for long. Tomorrow the king will come and finish us. I just hope that our defiance has bought the other barons enough time to gather their forces and allies to oppose this monster who calls himself a king.

Until the next life, farewell.

Henry De Montford

March 6th 1835

Richard Baker

———

John Stuart Mill, author, philosopher and a great advocate of a truly just society, had persuaded his friend Thomas Carlyle to let him read his newly completed work, Volume 1 of "The French Revolution: A History," before it went to the printer. Unfortunately, an unknowing servant mistook the pages of scrawled handwriting to be unimportant and used them to help light a fire.

When Betty answered her master's summons she felt good to know that J.S. would be warm on this cold morning.

But all was not as she had hoped. On entering J.S. Mill's study, he turned to Betty in a high state of anxiety and asked if she had happened upon any papers when she was in the room earlier. Poor Betty was dumbfounded when she realised what she had done with her master's precious notes. She burst into tears and confessed her error.

John Stuart Mill was shocked to the core, wondering how he would explain it to Thomas Carlyle, but, realising it was as much his fault as Betty's, and thinking philosophically, realised a few burnt papers were but a small concern compared with the French Revolutionary War, and could be replaced much easier than a monarch's head. He smiled at Betty and told her not to worry.

March 6th 1835

Caroline Atterwill

———

As Betty entered John's study, she saw the panic on his face and her mind immediately cast back to the previous evening. She scrambled her brain trying to think of any mistakes she had made but none came to mind.

With his hand, John gestured her to sit down, which she did carefully, knowing this was no everyday situation. His head turned slightly towards the fireplace and her scrambled brain started to adjust to terrifying reality, whilst thinking back to the screwed up balls of paper that had been turned to ash, and their eyes met.

Betty was not aware of what writing had existed on those pages she had burned early that morning but by John's expression alone she realised they were of great importance.

After John explained to Betty what she had done, she was mortified and feared she was about to lose her job. John stopped her in mid thought process and proceeded to ease her troubled mind with just a quick word and a hand on her shoulder and she realised not only her mistake but also his forgiveness.

Fourteen Years On

Ambrose Doherty

———

0   He was born in the Year of Our Lord 1962, not that he remembered the event.

14   At fourteen, he was quite the young scholar and Athletics, Football and Rugby his favoured endeavours.

28   Married by now with a young family but not for much longer he was soon to find out. Total chaos was to ensue.

42   The revelation that rocked his world was the discovery of a vile condition that was with him from the day he was born.

56   This is my current age and all I can say at this point through the progress of said vile condition is thank The Lord for the wonderful friends I now have.

70   Let it adorn any memorial I may receive that through all the ups and downs, numerous as they were, I did the best I could.

Fourteen Years On
Sean Nelson

———

0   Fortunate parents, this little dude slept well mostly, through the night. An intense observer through the day, finding provocative laughter never working for him.

14   Following on from the template of his early years, was introverted, shy, with two close friends and no others.

28   Has a fiancée now. Up and down relationship due to their chalk and cheese personalities.

42   Divorced. Two children. His wife and their differences took their toll.

56   An element of himself had opened up and after years in a humdrum job quit and went travelling.

70   One of his children has died tragically. Never forgave himself for lending her the car though it had failed its M.O.T.

Not A Typical Shop
Caroline Atterwill

———

I work in our family shop. It's not a typical shop such as a newsagents or a shoe shop. It's more odds and ends, things that aren't usually easy to find, things that are a bit different, and because we could get our hands on any object, we are very popular. I'll give you an example. Last week Mrs Brown walked through the door and there was sadness on her face and she told me her budgie had died and she wanted a small decorative little coffin for him, and a shoe box was definitely not fitting for Princess the budgie so I said I would have one for her in a couple of days. Time passed and she came in again, and from behind the counter I brought out a small gold box encrusted with precious jewels. She loved it and with great surprise paid above the asking price because she was so impressed.

Now that is just one example of the type of unusual things that people ask for, and nine times out of ten I produce the goods and people are in awe. No-one apart from the family knew how or where I could get these unusual items but that is the easiest part because at the end of the day, after I lock up, I go out the back where my portal appears and, just like magic, I jump through to whatever era I need and help myself to the past, even once taking a gold encrusted jewellery box from Queen Elizabeth I's dresser in 1580, which is not unlike the coffin that Princess lays in now. (How coincidental.)

Fantasy Shop
Gordon

———

I could buy the parents I never met.
I could buy the legs I lost.
I could buy the children I haven't seen for years.
I could buy the life I really wanted!
I could buy death or eternity at will.

I would buy compassion and love for everyone.
I would buy food to feed the world.
I would buy every single weapon used to destroy other people
and hide them for all eternity.

Map Out Your Future But Do It In Pencil

Ambrose Doherty

———

A s a haphazard, often enthusiastic, observer of human nature, I often find that things catch your eye at the time to coincide with your current state of mind and from an unexpected source. These rare occasions hold for me an extra fascination.

In bygone days of yore, or youth as it's now described, mapping out my future seemed to be the order of the day. So as was the norm, I followed suit.

As time with all its foibles proceeded on its unstoppable journey, with knowledge and "wisdom" acquired, my thoughts changed and outlooks upon future events became more a part of my thinking. Time became more relevant due to its diminishing nature.

Then a quote from the aforementioned source crossed the path of my journey and made me smile.

"Map out your future but do it in pencil."

God bless you, Jon Bon Jovi.

And To Close...

The Blades Aerobatic Team

———

Northampton Hope Centre is one of the charities supported by The Blades, a leading display team renowned worldwide. They invited the Creative Writing Group to attend one of their practice sessions at Sywell Airport and the members received great hospitality on April 11th 2019. They watched from the balcony of the Blades headquarters, met and chatted to the pilots, all of them ex-Red Arrows, and had a close up tour of the planes.

A Morning With The Blades

Caroline Atterwill

———

As the three pilots headed down the runway, the excitement was palpable. The skies were inviting, as if the universe had given them the all clear for this very occasion.

From sweeping to soaring in seconds, they flew in the skies like acrobats flying in perfect synchronicity. I felt my heart almost bursting through my ribcage, so to watch these pilots fly with such grace and magnificence with their hearts still intact was incredible. I could never have imagined such multiple experiences of senses, visual coupled with auditory, and vibration. They blew my mind. Over the years I've been on a fair few rollercoaster rides and, thinking back, I could never control my body jolting from side to side, up and down, let alone keeping in touch with the ground.

The power between their legs must be orgasmic and, accompanied with the orders you hear shouted down the headsets, is more than I can imagine. If you haven't yet watched them in action, no amount of words that I write will help you visualise their performance. As they are in flight, I am in awe. You find yourself struggling not to blink because you don't want to miss a thing.

From the first moment they hit the sky until the last as they landed, my attention was captured. The buzz of watching them was fantastic and won't be matched for a long time. They work beautifully as a team and their skill and timing were impeccable. They literally had their lives in each others' hands. I feel so privileged to have met some of England's heroes.

I Am

(From "Whalesong" by Judith Nicholls)

Richard Jones

———

I am
land walker,
pollution expert,
maker of mess and destruction.
I harm everything.
I know
the hum of nuclear reactors,
the crashing of falling trees
in the smoke of burning fossil fuels that WILL run out.
Of chemicals, the usefulness of which is outweighed
by the damage they do,
from dawn to dusk.
Yet I refuse to stop.
The stubbornness of Man.
I harm everything.

I Was Man

(From "Whalesong" by Judith Nicholls)

Sean Nelson

———

I was Man,
now I'm worse than beast.
Once I nurtured,
once I respected life and space around me.
Yes, I ate you beast.
Now I'm one of you.
But we have all turned on ourselves
and in turn are beasts.
Care, common decency, have diminished
as I've joined the club –
"Me, Myself, I,"
took the pledge to grab what I can
on this ball of rock,
while I'm still here,
regardless of consequences
or who I hurt.

Holy Sepulchre Church,
Friday January 25th 2019
Ambrose Doherty

———

As he walked into the venue all that struck him was the splendour within, knowing the reason for his presence here that night, and its significance enhanced his anticipation of events to unfold. Confident in the knowledge that all work to be shared that evening had been done, and yet as the paying customers began their arrival, with many faces recognisable, his thoughts turned towards his desire for success, as well as his hopes for his cohorts to shine. His focus was intense and his confidence assured. Time to begin.

Time at this point seemed to take upon itself to cease to exist as would normally occur and passed so differently, all too soon. Any fears of disaster dissolved with the echoes of applause.

He could get used to this, he thought!

Performance

Richard Baker

———

The man said, "Can you write?"

I said, "Yes and no," not knowing which was true. I guess they both were.

So the man said, "Be only positive," which I did.

I put words on paper, but was I writing anything constructive? Well, the man said, apparently, yes! But people say all manner of things, but if you are not sure the reason for your praise can elude you. But, okay, just.

Then the man said, "Your work is worthwhile. Can you read this in public?" and I said, "Maybe."

Then I found myself in front of an audience verbalising those words I had written. Then I remembered, before my life collapsed and I became homeless, I had done all these things before and had just forgotten I could!

Why?

Caroline Atterwill

———

Why is the grass green?
Why is the sky blue?
Why is me me?
Why is you you?
Why are pigs pigs?
Why are cows cows?
We ask why and what
And the whens and the hows
And forget just to live in the here and now.

Why is she black?
Why is he white?
Why is day day?
Why is night night?
Why is heat hot?
Why is ice cold?
Why is young young?
Why is old old?

All of these whys, we fill our minds
But only us, only mankind.
Our brains we mould and twist and bend
But at the end of the day, the end is the end.

So do the whys really matter
Or are we wasting our time?
Same way, pen put to paper,
I'm writing this rhyme.

Another life gone
And the whys start again.
More pointless time wasted
For us women and men.

I'm leaving you now
To go and get high
And now you can ask yourself,
Caroline,
Why?

Acknowledgements

———

All those writers who have attended the Creative Writing Group sessions during its seven years, for their participation and their sharing, with a special mention to "The Regulars," cornerstones of the group – Ambrose Doherty, Caroline Atterwill and Richard Jones.

Alan Moore, author, for his encouragement of the Creative Writing Group and for providing such a wonderful foreword for *Writing in Hope*.

Joe Brown, for co-ordinating our links with Alan.

Adam Blakemore, graphic designer, www.strelka.co.uk, for his expertise, support and unending patience in designing the cover and creating the layout of the book.

Belmont Press, Harlestone Road, Northampton for printing this volume.

Kim Edwards, Kall Kwik Northampton, for her assistance during the project.

Jo Blake, performer, www.jo-blake.co.uk, for storytelling at fund-raising evenings in Bradden and Northampton.

The Church of the Holy Sepulchre, Northampton, for providing the venue for the Northampton evening of readings and storytelling.

Michelle Hollis of Costa Coffee, Kingsthorpe, for inviting the group for a morning of coffee and writing.

The Blades Aerobatic Team for their superb hospitality when the group viewed a practice session at Sywell.

James Vollmar and Rosemary Sturge, authors, for sharing their experiences of publishing.

Northampton Hope Centre Art Group for enabling its members to express themselves creatively.

Robin Burgess, CEO, Hope Centre, for enthusiastically backing the book's publication.

Louise Danielczuk, Fundraising and Marketing Manager, Hope Centre, for her excellent support throughout the publication process, including responding to a myriad of emails!

Joanna McColgan, Case Worker, Hope Centre, for arranging Alan Moore's visit to the Creative Writing Group.

Dan McCulloch, Hope Centre volunteer, who filmed the evening at the Church of the Holy Sepulchre.

Lorna Robjohns, Hope Centre volunteer, for initiating the group, continuing to support it on a regular basis, and for generating sponsorship for the book project.

Dave Blake, Hope Centre volunteer, for leading the group sessions and compiling and editing *Writing in Hope*.

The Brethren of England's Centre Lodge, Northampton, are proud and delighted to have supported the members of the Northampton Hope Centre in creating this artistic collection of writings. We wish them every success in their future endeavours.

Special thanks go to Albert Wynne for organising the very generous donation from The Brethren of England's Centre Lodge, Northampton.

Thanks also for their financial support to Martin Neal of Northampton Builders Ltd.; James Cushing; and all those people who subscribed to *Writing in Hope* in advance of publication and attended fundraising events.

Dedication

———

This book is dedicated to all those, past and present, who have used Northampton Hope Centre and the former soup kitchen.